PRAISE
FLYING AGAINS

Captain Trochon is a true warrior,
no other to win his battle against cancer. After seventeen
years, he is still going strong while helping hundreds of
patients follow in his footsteps, giving them courage and
strength. The fight against cancer would be much faster if we
had more patients and advocates like him.

Prof. Valter Longo
Director of USC Longevity Institute, Los Angeles

Jean Jacques is one of the very special patients I had during
my career, and certainly in the top two. The first one is still
Bernard Giraudeau, a famous French actor, who lived with
kidney cancer for more than ten years and had these wonderful
words: "Since the time I had my cancer, life has never been so
bright, and I realized how everything is important," but he also
added: "We have to learn how to live with cancer, we cannot
fight cancer, we have to live with it." And he did.

Jean Jacques is a very different patient, and he never told
me that life was better since he had cancer, and he decided to
do everything he could to fight cancer.

Two different approaches, but so incredible. And JJ is
fighting every day, every minute, with all the qualities he used
as a pilot: checking everything, understanding everything
and retaining an incredible enthusiasm. This enthusiasm

convinced me that the ketogenic diet and metabolic treatment needed to be evaluated as a novel therapy for cancer. We organized Rethinking Cancer 2017 together and, since that time, I have been pushing oncologists to scientifically evaluate these therapeutic approaches. Results are coming and we will certainly know shortly.

But in the meantime, JJ will be there to ensure that the field is moving forward.

THANK YOU, JJ

Your friend, Bernard

Dr. Bernard Escudier
Institut Gustave Roussy, France

This work presents unique and important questions for medicine and cancer therapy woven into the narrative of a personal journey, touching aspects of life we can all relate to and culminating in a victorious fight against cancer. The book will appeal to a wide audience and marries educational endeavor with inquisitive dissection of the spirit of answering questions that some are scared to ask.

Dr. David Quinn
Medical Director, USC Norris Cancer
Hospital and Clinics, Los Angeles

JJ Trochon provides a riveting heartfelt story of grace, courage and recovery in his horrific battle with stage four malignant kidney cancer. He does a masterful job in weaving his life-long passions for aviation, rugby and surfing into his enduring struggle to manage and eventually overcome his affliction. His wife, Heather, and his father, along with other family members, are acknowledged for their roles in his recovery. Most importantly, JJ attributes the remarkable success in managing his cancer to several "pillars of health," including a ketogenic diet, water-only therapeutic fasting and a cyanobacterial biomass (spirulina), all of which selectively target the abnormal metabolism and blood vessels (angiogenesis) of malignant tumors. Also important for JJ's success was his avoidance of toxic radiation, chemotherapy and immunotherapy that can contribute to rapid tumor recurrence. Emerging scientific evidence shows that most, if not all, cancers suffer a common defect where fermentation replaces oxygen-dependent respiration for growth. The success of JJ's alternative approach to managing his metastatic tumors is consistent with the new understanding that cancer is primarily a metabolic disease that can be managed with non-toxic metabolic therapies. JJ Trochon is a pioneer and his memoir will offer hope to millions of cancer patients throughout the globe.

Prof. Thomas Seyfried
Professor of Biology, Boston College, Massachusetts

Qu'importe la destination ! c'est le chemin pour y arriver qui compte. Tout ce temps passé à connaître puis reconnaître le chemin en vol, une rétrospective fascinante. Tout le temps à venir à inventer le nouveau chemin, celui qui mènera à la continuité de la vie, dans sa beauté pour la nature, et l'amour pour les siens. Ce n'est pas de la guérison dont on parle, c'est un prétexte futile. Bravo Jean-Jacques, nous contemplons l'ascension de votre Himalaya.

Never mind the destination, it's the path leading there that counts. All that time spent getting to know and recognizing the flight path—a fascinating retrospective. All that time ahead in which to carve out a new path, the one leading to life continuing, with all its natural beauty and its loving relationships. We're not talking about a cure; that would be a pointless exercise. Bravo, Jean-Jacques, we're beholding your ascent to the summit of your own personal Himalayas.

(Translated from French)

Prof. Laurence Zitvogel
Professor of Immunology and Clinical
Biology Paris-Saclay University; Research Director
INSERM U1015, France

Most valuable, authentic, fascinating, lifesaving and motivating. A true call to take one's destiny into one's own hands … with a touch of candor that commands respect. Thank you for having written it.

Dr. Francoise Wilhelmi de Toledo
Director, The Buchinger Wilhelmi Clinic, Germany

FOREWORD BY WILLIAM W. LI, MD
New York Times bestselling author of *EAT TO BEAT DISEASE*

FLYING AGAINST ━•━ THE ━•━ ODDS

ONE MAN'S JOURNEY
TO NEW WAYS
OF HEALING

JEAN-JACQUES TROCHON
with Heather Whitehall-Trochon

Flying Against the Odds: One Man's Journey to New Ways of Healing
Published by Ikhaya Publishing
Copyright © 2021 by Jean-Jacques Trochon. All rights reserved.

ISBN: 978-2-9574675-0-1
Personal Memoir

Cover and Interior design by Victoria Wolf,
Wolf Design and Marketing
Cover photography by Florian Rayneau

www.jeanjacquestrochon.com

In Memory of My Dad

CONTENTS

FOREWORD

I FIRST MET JEAN-JACQUES TROCHON in the summer of 2012. He had recently undergone surgery to his right lung. As part of his recovery, JJ was researching into new cancer treatments and had come across my TED Talk in which I spoke about food as medicine to fight cancer, based on a scientific approach called "antiangiogenesis" that starves malignant cells. Wanting to find out more about antiangiogenic foods, he reached out to me. During our initial Skype conversation, I was amazed to hear that JJ was under the care of Dr. Bernard Escudier, a colleague from Paris with whom I had worked many years previously on new ways to treat kidney cancer. As we spoke further, it became clear that JJ had a vast breadth of knowledge on a wide range of innovative approaches to cancer. I listened with great interest because I've learned over my career that many times patients bring something important and unexpected to the table that can spark new ideas on how to better approach a disease, like cancer.

JJ is not your typical cancer survivor. He is a smartly focused and precise cancer warrior—the exact qualities that led to his soaring success as a pilot of commercial jumbo jets. Just as a pilot would, JJ defined his destination, studied different routes available to get him there, checked the local conditions and filed his flight plan for health. As he set out to beat kidney cancer, he assembled his crew of top physicians and scientists to help guide him and embarked on a journey based on methods that oncologists are only now beginning to appreciate: nutritional modification using whole foods and natural products, and fasting. Like his international team of medical specialists, JJ's background spans several continents and multiple fields of interest and languages. His natural curiosity about cancer turned fear into courage, and uncertainty into commitment. In 2017, he turned his commitment into action and, with my support, led the organization of a brilliant and groundbreaking conference we called Rethinking Cancer 2017. JJ is a pioneer in uniting leading experts from different fields around the goal of improving the way in which cancer is treated. The result: he conquered his disease while living a fulfilling life, making him a paragon for leading the fight against cancer using food. To his doctors, he is an amazing "odds-beater," having not just survived, but thrived despite his disease; to his friends, JJ is nothing short of an extraordinary human; to the readers of *Flying Against the Odds*, JJ and his story will surely be an inspiration. This book will show you how one man flew directly into the headwinds of cancer and, using the latest scientific data on nutrition as his Operating Manual, how he found new ways to land safely on his journey to healing.

William W. Li, MD
New York Times bestselling author of *Eat to Beat Disease*,
President and Medical Director,
The Angiogenesis Foundation

INTRODUCTION

WHEN I MET JJ IN 2006, we spoke about his cancer as a dark cloud that had passed briefly through his life. Back then we didn't anticipate its unwelcome reappearance on an otherwise untroubled horizon. Nor did we imagine it transforming into a mighty cumulonimbus, that most menacing of cloud formations associated with extreme weather, such as heavy torrential downpours, lightning or even tornadoes. No pilot wants to find himself flying into the eye of a cumulonimbus. But sometimes fate has other plans in store.

What we learned, as we were battered incessantly by the forces of nature, is that cancer, like the sudden onset of a storm, is indiscriminating. It can appear out of nowhere and strike anyone at any time, irrespective of age, color, gender or race. And, just like the lightning of that cumulonimbus, cancer can strike more than once.

As JJ has navigated his way through his own personal storm, I have been at his side in my role of "co-pilot." Only as a team is it possible to land safely when the going gets tough. Our shared journey has taught us to be vigilant, to always be prepared for an unexpected bump in the flight path ahead. In writing this book, we wanted to offer readers a plan with which to navigate those bumps.

This is JJ's story, but just as his cancer experience has been a shared journey, so was the production of this book. My role was to put his experience into words. I have been his silent witness, observing from the wings as he spent hour after hour sifting through the latest research into natural cancer therapies, slowly gathering his team of elite professionals at his side.

Teamwork is a recurring theme in JJ's memoir, as indeed it has been in his career as a pilot. He reached out to the very brightest minds in each of his fields of interest. And they responded with generosity and kindness, recognizing in JJ a man with an unquenchable thirst for knowledge and a blazing passion to share his insights.

But there's more to the story. Much more.

Newly married to JJ, I began to notice certain quirks to his personality. I would join him regularly on his flights but, whereas I loved to discover new places, to step away from the well-trodden tourist trail and dive with abandon into the unknown, he was happiest when staying in the sanitized comfort of the hotel. I put this down to fatigue, since the stopovers were generally no more than forty-eight hours, and he had just flown the plane, after all! However, back at home, he also liked to follow set routines and didn't really enjoy socializing. Nor did we often go to restaurants, since he preferred to regularly have the same meals and to eat them in our home environment.

Over the years of supporting my husband, nursing him through sickness and then aiding him in his recuperation, I became increasingly aware of his need for structure, of his almost obsessive desire to watch the daily news, both on American and French channels, as well as his relentlessness in pursuit of certain ideas. It wasn't behavior with which I'd had any experience, and it was the very opposite of my own. Sociable by nature, I love to find myself in unfamiliar surroundings, eating new types of food, going to the theater, to concerts, talking with strangers ... I was beginning to find our differences quite tricky to manage.

One day, speaking with an acquaintance, I discussed JJ's approach to life.

"Have you considered that he might have Asperger's syndrome?" she said, adding that her first husband was an "Aspie."

"Asp ... what?" I said, hearing the term for the first time.

However, something clicked, and I wanted to know more. That evening, I opened Google and started some research of my own. What I found was fascinating and a complete game-changer in terms of my marriage and understanding my husband.

I learned that, historically, some of the world's most brilliant thinkers are thought to have had Asperger's syndrome, a condition often referred to as high-functioning autism or, more recently, Autism Spectrum Disorder (ASD). Michelangelo, the famed Renaissance artist, is said to have been obsessive and to have followed repetitive routines. Indeed, so intense was his focus that he dedicated eight years of his life to laboring on *The Last Judgement*. Thanks to his highly retentive memory, he was also able to generate many hundreds of sketches for the ceiling of the Sistine Chapel.

Others suspected of having Asperger's include Abraham Lincoln, who apparently loved routine, was said to have a rigid nature, and also went on to become arguably one of the greatest presidents in America's history. Another is Wolfgang Amadeus Mozart, who, despite his social difficulties, was a music prodigy and wrote his first piece at the age of five. And then there's Albert Einstein, who didn't speak until the age of three but went on to develop the theory of relativity. Back then, it was not possible to officially diagnose these geniuses, since so little was known about autism at the time.[1]

More recently, evidence suggests that Steve Jobs, the visionary behind Apple, was on the autism spectrum. He was certainly obsessed with detail and considered to be a slave to perfectionism. Indeed, Apple's iconic "Think Different" campaign from the nineties, largely written by copywriter Rob Siltanen, plays homage to those brilliant minds who pave the way for others to follow:

"Here's to the crazy ones. The misfits. The rebels. The trouble-makers. The round pegs in the square holes. ... They push the human race forward. And while some may see them as the crazy ones, we

see genius. Because the people who are crazy enough to think they can change the world, are the ones who do."

As I connected the dots, I began to realize that my husband's own brilliant mind, his unyielding focus, clarity of thought and steely determination were traits most likely resulting from this condition, a condition that has often caused him to be misunderstood in a society that likes to place people in convenient "boxes," a society quick to stigmatize those wired to think differently. In my husband's case, it is this unique wiring that has enabled him to think above and beyond the proverbial box. And, ultimately, to save his life.

I must add that although JJ was unaware, until recently, that he might be on the spectrum, he has always felt "different" to other people. He has never been officially diagnosed, but we decided to both take a test that is commonly used to determine whether or not someone has Asperger's. The test was divided into three categories: 0–29 (no autism), 30–33 (possible autism) and 34 and above (autism likely). My score came out at five, meaning there was absolutely no trace of it, whereas JJ's score was at the other end of the scale. Even without the test, it was patently clear.

I have not written directly about my husband's condition in his memoir, since my own "light bulb" moment only occurred in the summer of 2019. (The memoir covers a significant period of his life from March 2003 to September 2017.) However, you will notice it in certain aspects of his behavior. For example, when he knows precisely how long a certain TED Talk lasts, right down to the number of seconds. Or when he refuses to give up while trying to make contact with a well-known doctor, but only reaches the doctor's personal secretary. After umpteen attempts, the secretary appears to metaphorically wave a white flag, and JJ is finally put through to the boss. It is also telling that JJ was unable to fit in with the French education system, which back then didn't allow for anyone whose behavior was considered unconventional. It was only once he was sent to finish his schooling in America that he started to flourish. Even to this day, he still talks about his schooling in France as a miserable time in his life.

Despite not specifically mentioning Asperger's or ASD in the memoir itself, I felt that his story would not be complete or honest if I didn't use my introduction to shine a light on this part of him that makes him special. As well as making him an extremely professional pilot, able to work within a tight structure requiring absolute precision and unemotional decision-making, his very particular way of thinking has enabled him to assimilate with ease the latest scientific findings and to combine approaches for optimum results. It is this specific ability that sets him apart from most other cancer patients, along with his steadfast refusal to accept that there is no cure for the disease. Despite a stage four cancer diagnosis in 2012, JJ is determined to beat the odds that have often been stacked against him. He is determined to be the exception rather than the rule. His story and his unique approach continue to give hope to others in his position.

To date, I have witnessed hundreds of people worldwide reach out to my husband. Indeed, not a day goes by without someone contacting him, asking for his help to guide them through their own cumulonimbus storm. Not only cancer patients, but also doctors from around the globe, all with questions to which today's medicine doesn't hold all the answers. JJ's personal story and his ability to explain often complex science in an easily comprehensible way have made him a point of reference for many.

Both JJ and I are aware that dark clouds may still be ahead, but we are also able to see beyond them. It is this message of optimism that we would like to share with you, the reader. But, for now, fasten your seatbelts and prepare to take flight with us.

Heather Whitehall-Trochon
Biarritz, August 2020

CHAPTER 1

Seeing Red

MARCH 2003

My parents were of the generation committed to making relationships work. Even when times were tough, there was never any question of giving up. My dad had been a fighter pilot, and both of my grandfathers had been decorated heroes. They were all men of great courage, men to whom I'd looked up and admired.

So, one day when I'd met my brother for lunch in Paris and told him I was getting a divorce, all I could feel was a deep sense of shame. Jean-Yves had looked at me, his eyes full of brotherly love and concern, offering words of support while reassuring me that he and the rest of our family were there for me. But our conversation only served to heighten my acute sense of failure. It was like an insidious rot seeping through every vein in my body.

As the oldest of three, I had always tried to do the right thing, to act as a role model for my siblings. And I felt that I was letting everyone down. It hurt like hell, but I couldn't keep pretending that everything was okay. I had desperately tried to make my marriage work, to the point that I was on the verge of a mental and physical breakdown. I was just one step away from falling over the precipice into a very dark place from which I might not be able to return.

My job as an airline pilot involved lots of unsociable hours and many nights spent away from my wife and children. When I returned home, it wasn't always easy to slot right back into the family routine of school runs, regular mealtimes and social activities. As is the experience of many pilots, I often just wanted to be left alone to catch up on sleep. Before long, my job had put a tremendous strain on the relationship, and I'd found myself becoming another sad statistic. I will never forget seeing the suffering on the innocent faces of my children as I picked up my bags and left the family home. Even thinking about it now, so many years later, takes me back to a very somber place.

Sitting in traffic that afternoon after lunch with my brother, I reflected on the slow and tragic unraveling of my existence. On how I had fallen from being the "golden boy," a dashing young pilot with the picture-perfect family living in a picture-perfect home. Nestled in an affluent commuter belt community, with its manicured lawns and golf club memberships, it was a home that I'd worked so hard to pay for and had often sacrificed being with my family in the process. And now, at the age of forty-one, my life had been reduced to that of a soon-to-be-divorced, morose, and lonely man.

Stuck in bumper-to-bumper traffic, I felt myself becoming increasingly agitated. The headache that came with the worst cold I'd ever experienced had returned with nagging persistence, gnawing sickeningly at my brain like a colony of ants on a jar of honey. I reached down to grab a bottle of the heavy-duty aspirin I'd carried with me and popped a couple more. All I wanted to do was to be back home and tucked up in bed. Home ... ha! I didn't even know where that was anymore. For now, I was renting an old, worn-out dwelling on a scruffy piece of farmland that, apart from a cluster of rabbit hutches and chicken coops, was otherwise uninhabited. The soulless four walls in which I was temporarily "living" were situated near the top of a hill at the end of a narrow, twisting lane that led away from a small, nondescript village. Devoid of the charm usually associated with the French countryside, this abode was cloaked in an omnipresent layer of gloom. It wasn't the kind of spot in which people just happened to "drop by" for a chat—a fact that suited me just fine.

Since the separation, I'd pretty much isolated myself from everyone. All I wanted to do was to be left alone or to work as much as possible. At least when I worked, I didn't have as much time to beat myself up.

Gripping tightly onto the steering wheel during that interminable drive, I let out a cry of frustration. Somewhat embarrassed at this sudden need to release stress, I cast my eyes furtively at my fellow drivers. Nobody seemed to have noticed.

I imagined that I was surrounded by happy people, all living in their own perfect bubbles and looking forward to going home to their loved ones. Home to the chatter of their children and to the welcoming smell of dinner being prepared by their attentive other half. All that awaited me was the miserable smell of rising damp in the hovel that had become my refuge from the world. To call it "home" only added to my despair, and yet I had chosen to live there in my self-imposed exile from the rest of society.

Just thinking about the place made me sadder and more depressed. The house belonged to a local farmer. I had taken on the lease without even caring what the place looked like. As it transpired, the building had been totally neglected and was undeniably remote, surrounded by nothing but fields and forests. I hadn't cared at the time, since I felt it was what I deserved. It had suited my needs. I merely wanted somewhere to sleep, to eat and to watch rugby on TV.

Sport was the one thing that brought me any kind of peace. That and seeing my kids. I had hoped that they would enjoy coming to see me in the forest, thinking they might view it as some kind of adventure. I'd imagined we would kick a ball around in the field in front of the house. But it hadn't worked out like that. They had only visited on a few occasions; the spot was just too isolated. My daughter, Kelly, was thirteen, and her brother, Jeff, eleven. They wanted to have sleepovers with their friends, not to spend nights with their depressed father in a house that made them scared on account of the eerie sound of its creaking floorboards and rattling window panes.

Still driving home and hoping to change my mood, I turned on the radio. I had stopped listening to music soon after my separation because the songs always seemed to be about relationships going wrong, making me feel even more wretched.

I preferred traffic bulletins or the weather forecast rather than my favorite titles from the Eagles or America, groups whose songs had been my personal soundtrack to happier times. The emotionless voice of the newscaster restored a sense of calm, enabling me to focus on nothing but the road ahead.

That's when a dull pain arose in my side. It reminded me of what it felt like when a surfboard slammed into me after I'd misjudged a wave. I'd been surfing since I was a kid, learning on the island of Tahiti at the age of seven, when my father had been stationed there for a few years. Nothing is more thrilling than catching the perfect wave, but you also learn to respect the power of the ocean. A surfboard can become a lethal weapon if you lose control of it, as many a surfer—myself included—has found out to their cost.

The pain disappeared as quickly as it had arrived, but I started to feel hot; sweat beaded on my forehead. My first thought turned to food poisoning. *The seafood at lunch? A reaction to the aspirin?* I didn't know the cause, just that I needed to get back to my place, fast. Luckily, as if a gift from the heavens, the traffic finally started to move.

I don't remember much about the rest of the journey

but, somehow, I made it up that farm track to the sad-looking house at the end. And not a moment too soon, since the burning sensation had now spread out across my groin. A persistent throbbing had appeared in the lower part of my back, joining forces with the unpleasant wave of nausea that had been rolling through my abdomen for the past half hour. I had kept trying to push it away, but my mind was now going crazy as I tried to make sense of everything.

What the hell is happening to me?

The car's engine had barely shuddered to a halt when I leapt out and slammed the door behind me. In my stressed state, I struggled to turn the key in the rusty lock of the house door. I was losing valuable seconds. It finally budged. Once inside, adrenalin kicking in, I flung my coat to the ground and rushed to the bathroom. The shock of what happened next still makes me shudder.

Bright red blood. An alarming fire-extinguisher red, which was practically glowing against the stark white of the toilet bowl. I had blood in my urine. Or, to be more precise, urine in my blood! In a moment of absolute clarity, I knew that I was in serious trouble. I soon learned that my kidney was failing.

I felt my legs folding beneath me. Grasping blindly for the wall, I tried to steady myself against the cold, avocado-colored tiles. For a few seconds, I must have stopped breathing, because I began gulping for air. Hyperventilating.

Dizzy with shock, I adopted a crouching position on the floor. I started to retch and could taste the bile rising up from my stomach. I broke out into a cold sweat, but stopped short of vomiting. I must have stayed that way for a couple of minutes, waiting for the nausea to pass, before dragging myself upright. Resting my forearms against the adjacent bathroom sink, I cupped my hands under the tap and splashed cold water against my face. It was then that I glanced up to the mirror. The reflection staring back at me was grim.

Along with the pain came an overwhelming wave of loneliness. I was acutely aware that nobody would hear me if I called for help.

Was my body now punishing me for having messed up? Finishing the job of self-flagellation that I'd started when I chose to live in this miserable place?

The bleak reality of my situation slammed brutally into my consciousness. I had a sudden yearning for the familiarity of my old life. It now seemed more out of reach than ever. For a moment, I bore the full force of my isolation and almost allowed it to drag me further down into the despair. But I somehow found an inner strength and pulled myself together. If only for the sake of my children, I had to survive.

A few minutes later, I had grabbed a few essential belongings and managed to call a friend, who agreed to alert the hospital of my imminent arrival. I knew that I had to get myself there. And fast. I didn't have time to wait for an ambulance. I didn't understand what was going on, but I knew it was serious. Stumbling back along the entrance hall, I lunged at the front door and rushed back to my car.

Tugging on the car door handle, the pain behind my kidney was now almost more than I could bear. I lowered my warring body gingerly down onto the driver's seat. Again, the face staring back at me in the mirror was that of a stranger. My eyes were sunk deeply into darkened hollows, the result of many sleepless nights.

Photographs of my children peered at me from the dashboard. Once more I had the feeling that I was failing them, just as my own body appeared to be failing me.

I then caught sight of a series of stuffed toy animals lodged in the space behind the front windshield. Simple tourist souvenirs, purchased during a family holiday in a South African game reserve, served as a poignant reminder of happier times.

Was it really so long ago? What happened to that life? Will I ever feel happy and at peace again?

My silent questions hung in the air unanswered, but I couldn't afford to dwell on my predicament. I needed help.

The car's engine grunted into action. Now I was doing things automatically, the captain in me taking over. The sound of my car was the only noise to disturb the ominous silence in this forgotten corner of the world. Despite my distress, I knew I had to navigate the overgrown path with caution.

My early flying years had been spent in Africa. I had fallen in love with the wilderness of the bush, even taking the first steps toward qualifying as a game ranger. The experience had taught me that an animal could run out of the forest at any moment. Of course, there are no elephants in northern France—but even a young deer or wild boar can cause a lot of damage to an oncoming vehicle.

Finally out on the road, I experienced further shockwaves spreading throughout my body. My kidney had taken on the guise of an angry internal volcano, ready to explode at any moment. Reaching a particularly sharp turn, the sheer pain of the maneuver made me cry out. It was then that I become aware of tears streaming down my face. Ashamed, I wiped them away with the back of my hand. My vision temporarily blurred, it was all I could do to stop the car from swerving into one of the countless trees lining this seemingly endless stretch of road.

Get a grip, man. Keep going. You're almost there.

These words became my mantra as I tried to concentrate on the way ahead. The clinic was about a twenty-minute drive from the house, but at that moment it may as well have been in another country. The road stretched out monotonously in front of me, my strength evaporating with every passing mile. I tried to imagine that I was wearing the *maillot jaune* in the Tour de France, the crowds were cheering ...

Only five more to go. Come on. You can do it.

I could feel my eyes tearing up again as I finally saw a sign for the nearby town of Chantilly and its *Clinique des Jockeys*.

Situated some twenty-five miles outside Paris, Chantilly is a pretty little town famous for its porcelain and lace. It is also home to the prestigious racecourse which annually hosts the glamorous *Prix de Diane* horse race in June. Such is the importance of horse racing in the area that the clinic is dedicated to the riders, many of whom are indebted to its services in mending their broken bones. The clinic to which

I was headed is basically a cottage hospital and not set up to deal with emergencies of this kind. However, I didn't have time to worry about the implications of that detail.

Holding on just long enough, I swerved into the clinic's car park. There was a crunching of brakes, and the car came to an abrupt stop. Laying my head on the wheel, I couldn't even summon the force to open the car door. Fortunately, a medical team was on standby, ready to put their underused skills into action. Someone opened the car door, and I was vaguely aware of a voice attempting to reassure me.

"Monsieur Trochon? Monsieur Trochon?"

I merely nodded in reply. Even the slightest movement was almost too much effort. Looking at me with genuine concern was a wiry man in his mid-forties and of Middle Eastern appearance. Judging from his white hospital coat, I assumed him to be some kind of doctor or even a surgeon.

"Monsieur Trochon, my name is Doctor Soussi," he said. "I am the on-duty urologist," he continued. "Don't worry. We are going to take good care of you."

My relief was overwhelming. I would have embraced him, if only I'd had the strength.

(Ironically, Soussi is pronounced the same as "souci," which, in my native French, means "worry." Doctor Worry was telling me not to worry! In any other circumstances, the irony of this would have brought a smile to my face. At that moment I was past caring.)

A team of orderlies helped me out of the car. They eased me onto a mobile bed, taking charge of my car keys in the process. Somebody parked my car out of harm's way, since it must have looked as though it had been abandoned at the scene of a hit and run.

The orderlies then wheeled me off in the direction of the clinic. As I was about to be pushed through the double doors of the emergency entrance, a plane roared overhead. I glanced upward at the familiar sound just in time to see an Airbus A320 in the knife-gray sky. It was a comforting sight, since this beautiful machine was the very model that I had been flying for the past six years. Ironically, the clinic was situated directly below the flight path to Charles de Gaulle airport, my place of work. There could be no mistaking the distinctive red, white and blue of the Air France insignia on the tail wing of the aircraft. And then the silver bird disappeared from view, leaving only a rapidly disintegrating vapor trail in its wake.

Is it a sign? Will I wear my stripes again?

At that moment I couldn't even have sat behind the controls of a child's carousel ride, let alone an Airbus A320. However, I grasped onto the positive image of the overhead plane with the fervor of a pilgrim seizing an amulet of holy water at Lourdes. Whatever was happening to me, I would not let it beat me. I told myself that I would resume command of that aircraft. With this empowering thought circulating through my mind, the double doors came together behind me with a definitive swoosh.

I closed my eyes and awaited my fate.

CHAPTER 2

My Blood Is Green

OSCAR WILDE, the nineteenth-century poet and playwright, is famously quoted as saying, "Rugby is a game for barbarians played by gentlemen." These words still hold true today. I can think of no other sport in which grown men with minimal body protection tackle each other on the field like raging bulls, only to transform into the kindest, most humble and polite men you are ever likely to meet—once they've stepped away from the flying mud and bestial grunting.

This game of gentlemen, in which two teams compete for control of an oval ball, is said to have started at Rugby School in England. Legend has it that, in 1823, a certain William Webb Ellis first ran with the ball, unwittingly laying the foundation for what would become the game as it is played today.

Ellis died in France in 1872, and his grave is cared for by the French Rugby Football Union—such is the importance of his contribution to the sport.

My own love of rugby began at around the age of thirteen, when I played as either fullback or winger for the school team of Saint Martin de France, in the French city of Pontoise. My favorite team was—and still is—South Africa's Springboks. As a youngster, I would accompany my dad on his flights to Johannesburg. If a match happened to be on at the time, it would be reported on the main radio stations and in the most popular newspapers. (Note: Television was only introduced to South Africa in 1976.) It was impossible not to be infected by the boisterous enthusiasm of the fans celebrating in the streets surrounding our hotel.

Later, as a young pilot myself, I would make it a point to request flights to Johannesburg so that I could catch a game at the legendary Ellis Park. I was always struck by the inclusive nature of the sport. Entire families, from the youngest toddler through to the oldest grandparent, would turn out to support their team, and it wasn't just the game that mattered. It was all about the camaraderie—both before, during and after the match. Fights between rival fans are pretty much unheard of in the rugby world. Supporters are not separated in the stands, and followers of losing teams are often seen buying beers for fans of the winners or, in the case of a South African game, sharing a typical *boerewors* sausage from the *braii* or grill. It is this community atmosphere that has always made me love the game so much. So much, that I had developed a personal involvement with the Springboks, or *Bokkies* as they are known to their fans.

In 1999, Wales hosted the Rugby World Cup with some of the games being played outside the country. England had been drawn to play the quarter-finals against South Africa in Paris. With such an exciting match set to occur virtually on my doorstep, I couldn't let the opportunity pass me by. I just had to get involved

⸺⸺⸺

I had started to make connections with the South African rugby community near the end of the 1980s. A decade later, I was already known in rugby circles and amongst my colleagues as the "rugby-mad" pilot. (I would ask for my tea to be served in the cockpit in a Springboks supporter's mug, and I often announced the scores of important games to passengers during flights.) With my characteristic dogged determination, I used my contact with friends at the South African Rugby Federation to get in touch with Nick Mallett, who was head coach of the Springboks at the time, and asked if I could help out in any way during the lead up to the Paris game of that World Cup tournament. Much to my delight, he accepted my offer of free labor and local knowledge. And that's how I found myself organizing two days of golf for the team in their leisure time.

My collaboration with the Springboks has gone from strength to strength since 1999. Many of the players and management are now firm friends. We have a mutual respect for one another, which is why I was so honored when they asked me to assist as a liaison officer at the Under-19 Rugby World Cup to be held in Paris in April 2003.

An annual junior level tournament for players up to the age of nineteen, the Under-19s acted as a springboard for the professional league. Organized by the sport's governing body, the International Rugby Board (IRB), it was an important event since it was where the agents spotted young talent for professional clubs. (In 2008, the Under-19s was merged into an event called the IRB Junior World Championship and is now for players under the age of twenty. The merger was a strategic decision taken to narrow the gap between juniors and seniors at a professional level.)

In the run-up to the 2003 event, blissfully unaware of my impending health crisis, I had been involved in the logistics and tasked to find suitable training grounds and once again organize activities for the boys. During the three-week-long tournament, I was slated to be on hand to help out as required, which could have meant anything from acting as a chauffeur through to preparing the changing rooms for the forthcoming "battle" by laying out the team's rugby jerseys, making sure that medical supplies were on hand and generally putting in place everything the players required for the match. I already had taken time off of work to ensure I would be available. But with the tournament starting in less than two weeks, this no longer seemed possible on account of my poor physical state.

Following my undignified appearance at the Clinique des Jockeys, I was hastily transported to a nearby hospital, where orderlies rushed me in for a scan. After the procedure, I sat opposite the radiologist as he pored over the results. I could tell by the look on his face that all was not well. Sure enough, he informed me that I had a large growth on my kidney, requiring immediate removal. However, something else was bothering him.

"The tumor is very advanced," he said, "but it doesn't really explain the bleeding. Did you have any other symptoms?"

I told him that I'd had a bad cold and had been taking a lot of aspirin over the previous three days.

A flash of recognition crossed his face as he looked me directly in the eyes. "Well, that could have saved your life," he said. "Had the tumor gone unnoticed for much longer, it might well have been too late. ... You are very lucky indeed," he added, shaking his head in disbelief.

(It turns out the excessive use of aspirin can cause hemorrhaging. Although not generally a desired side effect, I was glad to have been alerted to my condition by this particular "red flag.")

My operation was scheduled to take place back at the Clinique des Jockeys. After having been driven back, again by ambulance, getting checked in and then meeting with my surgeon, I can't really say that "lucky" was the first word to spring to mind. In my book, Doctor Landé was disturbingly close to my own age. I felt concern about putting my life in his relatively young hands. I then imagined that this could be how my passengers sometimes reacted when they saw me as their "young" captain. A few probably had questioned my ability to take charge of a plane, just as I now questioned Doctor Landé's ability to operate on me.

In a no-nonsense manner, the surgeon sat down to speak to me about my condition and what to expect in the forthcoming surgery.

"You've got aggressive kidney cancer," he said in a calm voice trained to reassure, despite delivering words that landed in my head like grenades. "The tumor is seven centimeters in length, and malignant," he continued, as though he were telling me something that he thought I already knew.

The news came as a shock. I hadn't had any pain until now, and I'd somewhat naively been hoping that the growth was benign. Just as I was digesting this information, he threw in another verbal missile. "I'm afraid I'll need to perform a nephrectomy, in other words, removal of the kidney in its entirety. This is necessary to prevent the cancer from spreading to other organs."

Nephrectomy. Malignant. Cancer. The words slammed around in my brain as I tried to connect them with something that would enable me to understand. Still, I drew a blank. I don't know what I had been expecting, since I was already aware of the tumor, but I just couldn't associate the word *cancer* with my own physical being. Cancer was something that happens to other people. To the ones with shaven heads and pitifully frail bodies. To the ones looking sad and frightened on those television commercials seeking funding for research. Not to someone like me, a runner and a surfer. It wasn't so long ago that I had participated in the world's longest cross-country skiing race, the Vasaloppet in Sweden. How could I have gone from peak physical fitness to having a malignant, potentially life-threatening disease? In truth, I hadn't been this scared since 1991, when I'd had to deal with another potentially explosive situation over which I'd had little control.

I had been with Air France for less than two years at the time. Back then I was a co-pilot on the A300, a plane that transported some three hundred passengers to cities throughout Europe. We had been en route to Damascus, Syria, just flying over the coast of Lebanon, when we'd received a call from air traffic control telling us to contact Air France Paris. Although I'd trained for it, a call like this is not a routine procedure, and I knew right away that something was wrong.

Sure enough, we were told that we may have a bomb on board our plane, and that the information was considered to be reliable. We needed to divert the plane and land as quickly as possible. When given this kind of message, protocol dictates that you don't ask questions but simply act upon what you've been told. Twenty minutes later, we were in Beirut, parked well away from the main terminal.

Much of what happened that day is a blur, but I will never forget the sight of some thirty military personnel, armed with what appeared to be Kalashnikovs, surrounding the plane. I remembered how impressive the men had looked in their uniforms. We were told that these soldiers were members of President Hafez al-Assad's private security corps, the kind you didn't want to mess with. We were ordered to disembark from the plane, passengers and crew alike, while the soldiers checked for a bomb on board.

As it turned out, we were given the all-clear, but the tension of that moment undoubtedly left a lasting impression on everyone concerned. The crew and I felt a sense of powerlessness, as we'd had to surrender our plane to Assad's men. I felt the same helplessness when facing Doctor Landé, but this time the bomb was ticking away in my own body, and all I could do was put my faith in the surgeon and his ability to diffuse it.

A few moments of silence passed as I digested the surgeon's sobering message. I hadn't asked any questions when first told about the tumor, since the contrast fluid used in the scan had made me lightheaded and nauseated. At this point, I was too weak to go into lengthy discussions about possible alternatives to surgery, and so, in that moment, I accepted my fate. I just wanted the pain to go away and the cancer to be taken out of my body. However, before the surgeon left, I reached out and tugged at his sleeve. I wanted him to promise me one thing.

"Doctor, just make sure it's a decent scar," I said. "I'm a surfer. I want people to believe me when I say I'd been attacked by a shark ... and survived!"

Doctor Landé smiled and then left the room, and so did my bravado.

I spent the next few hours sending messages about my sudden change of circumstances to my employer, my family, and friends. I even managed to speak to my children. I could hear the worry in their voices. The conversation left me feeling sad, since I felt that I was repeatedly letting them down, but it also made me more determined than ever to get this ordeal over with and return to being their father. I longed more than anything to take them up in the cockpit again, so that they could feel proud of me once more.

Before attempting to get some sleep, I had one final, but very important task ahead. I needed to contact the management of the South African Under-19 rugby team. As I typed an email to Butch Watson-Smith, general manager of all teams of the South African rugby federation and number three in the organization's hierarchy, I once again felt that I was letting people down, not least of all the players. I knew that everyone is replaceable, but I also knew that it wouldn't be so easy to find someone to fulfill my role at such short notice. I just hoped that the management and the team would understand.

The email that I received back from Butch, less than one hour later, totally blew my mind. Writing to me, he revealed the confidential information that South Africa's slogan for the Rugby World Cup, to be played in Australia later that autumn, was set to be *Our Blood Is Green*. Planned soon to be splashed on advertising throughout South Africa, it alluded to the green of the team's jerseys and was also a means of uniting people of different creed and color.

Butch wrote, "We are all with you, JJ. And I have absolutely no doubt that when the surgeon opens you up tomorrow, he will see that your blood is green." The image resonated with me. I took it in as a life-enforcing metaphor, one that I would grip onto throughout my cancer journey. Even today, "My blood is green" means that I am not alone, that I have the full strength of my rugby family behind me.

Butch must have informed the tight-knit rugby fraternity of my impending operation because my email in-box soon was flooded with messages of support from several players and coaches from teams around the world. These words of comfort from people I idolized reinforced my will to live. I might have messed up in my marriage, but I had a great many friends out there who still believed in me.

Taking comfort in the kindness of so many, I swallowed the sedatives prescribed earlier by the anesthetist. A dreamless sleep followed. I awoke a few hours later to the sound of a cart and rattling bottles. It was similar to the sound of the drink cart being pushed through the business class cabin of my aircraft. However, these present bottles contained a potent assortment of sedatives and painkillers. The harsh glare of the overhead strip-light was also designed more for efficiency than a gentle awakening.

I checked the clock. It was five in the morning. I saw the nurse approach, and I knew now was the time to steel myself for what was to come—that I was about to face what would perhaps be the most difficult challenge of my life, and all of it heralded by what, in any other circumstance, would be the most benign phrase, "Good morning, Mr. Trochon. We are ready for you now."

CHAPTER 3

Toward the Light

MUCH HAS BEEN WRITTEN about the so-called near-death experience or NDE—a term first coined in 1975 by psychiatrist Raymond Moody in his book *Life after Life*. While reports of NDEs go back to antiquity, the oldest medical record of such an experience is said to be included in the *Anecdotes de Médecine* written by French military physician Pierre-Jean du Monchaux in 1740. NDEs take many different forms, but often are associated with a reported experience of the afterlife and God.

Despite being sent to Catholic schools and also making the obligatory childhood Sunday visit to church whenever we stayed with my grandparents, I can't say that I have particularly strong religious beliefs. Nevertheless, I like to keep an open mind about faith and have always treated NDEs in much the same way.

Maybe a logical, scientific explanation exists for such things? Some modern researchers say that sensations associated with NDEs can be explained by a lack of blood and oxygen flow to the brain. Whatever the truth may be, my own experience made such an impression on me that many years passed before I was prepared to talk about it.

Like most reports, I can only describe it as an overriding sense of peace. I had been floating in a tunnel-like space, bathed in light. The light had radiated warmth and love, giving me the sensation of being protected. I felt neither pain nor fear at my situation. In the distance I saw a tall figure who appeared to be glowing in an ethereal, dare I say it, heavenly way?

The one element of my experience that seems different than what I've read was that the figure was telling me to go back. The communication had been nonverbal, but was nonetheless unambiguous. Unlike many others who've had NDEs, I had not been given a choice as to whether I would cross over or go back to my life. I felt I was being told that my time hadn't yet come—that I still had a purpose to fulfill.

If someone else had recounted this to me, I probably would have laughed it off. I mean, it's the ultimate cliché you see in so many films. Yet, in my mind, there is no question that what I experienced was real. I woke up in the post-op recovery room in the full knowledge that I had been sent back to live my life. I didn't have long to dwell upon what had just happened, because I was brought back to the physical world by the sound of a voice.

"Mr. Trochon ...? Can you hear me?"

My eyelids were still closed, but I became aware of someone hovering over me. I could feel their breath warm against my cheek. I tentatively opened my eyes and was able to discern a face. Both the face and the voice belonged to a nurse. She was dressed in blue scrubs that made a rustling sound as she leaned over my bed. Mingling with the scent of antiseptic was a subtler hint of rose, which was a comfort to me in the otherwise sterile surroundings. The nurse gently lifted my wrist and took my pulse. Satisfied that all was well, she nodded and made a couple of notes on the clipboard attached to the bottom of my bed. It had taken a few seconds for my situation to sink in, but slowly things became ordered in my mind.

My kidney had been removed, or at least I assumed that it had. When I attempted to move my arm to touch the small of my back, I found that I was unable to do so. Not only was my movement hindered by numerous tubes protruding awkwardly from various parts of my body, but also I was still under the influence of the drugs that I'd been administered.

When I tried to speak to ask how things had gone, I couldn't string the words together. I heard them form in my head, but they came out jumbled as though I were drunk. The effort proved to be too much, and I felt my eyelids closing again. Resistance was futile. I thankfully took refuge in sleep.

I don't know how long I was out for, but I stirred, as I

again felt a hand touching my own. This time the hand was smaller, that of a child. Opening my eyes with tremendous difficulty, I realized that I was back in my hospital room. I glanced down to see my daughter, Kelly, caressing my arm. Her brown eyes were saturated with worry, making her appear much older than her thirteen years.

I saw, standing at the foot of the bed, my blond-haired son. In contrast to his sister, Jeff looked small and vulnerable. He had inherited the penetrating blue eyes of my own father. Those eyes looked back at me now, willing me to speak, to reassure him that everything was going to be okay.

It was Kelly who broke the silence, flinging her arms around my neck. Jeff began to cry. It must have been a shock for my kids to see me like this, attached to strange machines and dressed in a hospital gown. They were more accustomed to my being in control of everything, wearing my dark blue pilot's uniform and commanding an airplane.

"Come here, my boy," I mumbled. It was hard to talk. My throat was parched, and my body pumped full of drugs. "Daddy had a nasty lump growing on his kidney. It's all gone now. I'm going to get better soon."

At least that's what I'd intended to say, but I doubt those words came out, since Jeff said nothing in response. He just stared at me with anxiety written all over his face.

Now, thinking back to this shy and vulnerable boy, I feel so proud of the impressive young man that Jeff has become. At just twenty, he left France behind to experience life on the other side of the world in Australia. He is, as of this writing, managing an award-winning café in Sydney's upmarket Double Bay area, and exudes an air of confidence in all that he does.

Back then, Kelly was the one who took charge of things and was very much the big sister, especially since the separation from my ex. A real tomboy, my daughter is also a determined young lady and has a hugely caring heart. Kelly is happiest when walking alone through a forest or driving her motorbike a little faster than she should. She was the same as a teenager, always testing the boundaries and getting into trouble at school. Jeff followed her lead in most things back then. I worried about my children becoming mixed up with the wrong crowd, without me there to keep an eye on things.

That first morning at the hospital, I couldn't have felt prouder of both children. With great difficulty, I struggled to prop myself up. Kelly soon had matters in hand; like a mini-nurse, she pressed a button to lift the upper part of the bed a little. She then plumped up my pillows and raised a water bottle to my mouth. Only her scrubbed, freckled face and ponytail revealed her true age. I took a couple of sips of water through a straw; the effort of doing so made me sink back in exhaustion. Looking at Jeff and Kelly, my mind momentarily drifted to a happier time, not so long before, when we had all been together on holiday in Cape Town, South Africa. It had been the first time that we had traveled as a unit of three, following my separation from their mother. To be honest I had felt apprehensive about it, not knowing how to keep my young children entertained, since this task had more often been my wife's domain. As a newly single dad, I was desperately trying to prevent myself from sinking into despair and struggling with the added pressure of showing my kids a good time.

The colorful mini-golf course in the coastal town of Muizenberg had saved the day. It overlooked the beach where I had first taught my children to surf a few years earlier. We spent many carefree hours hitting a ball around and having fun together. My memories of that day are still vibrant—the saltiness of the sea, the screeching of gulls, and the contagious laughter of my son and daughter.

Still woozy from the operation, I can't remember too much more of my children's visit. I was vaguely aware of someone—their mother?—calling them. A nurse then ushered them out of the room to allow me to rest. Before leaving, Kelly and Jeff each planted a kiss on my cheek. It was only when I was alone once more that I allowed a couple of tears to roll down my face. My tears were a mixture of sadness and anger at my situation. I was more determined than ever to beat this cancer and be the best father possible.

Once my kids had left, I noticed a pile of rugby magazines stacked on my bedside table. (I was later told that some of my friends had popped in to say hello, but I have no recollection of their visits.) Using all my strength, I grabbed the top magazine and started to weakly flick through the pages. Panicking, I realized that I could barely make out the headlines. The words beneath them were blurred and scrambled. I rubbed at my eyes and strained to read, but it was hopeless.

At first, I assumed that I was just tired from the operation and my sight would get back to normal in the coming days. Unfortunately, that didn't prove to be the case. In fact, I would never again have the perfect vision that I had enjoyed prior to my surgery. I have since learned this is a side effect that occurs in some cases.

The next twenty-four hours saw me drifting in and out of sleep, but slowly the cocktail of sedatives and painkillers started to wear off. I don't have adequate words to describe the agony I felt when I finally regained full consciousness. It was beyond excruciating, as though my left side had been slashed open. And, of course, that is pretty much what had happened, although I'd assumed it had been done with precision and then neatly sewn together again. So fresh after the operation, I couldn't bear to look at the area causing so much pain. In desperation, I pressed an alarm dangling above my head. After what seemed like an eternity, a stressed-looking nurse arrived.

"Please help me!" I begged. "The pain. I can't bear it ..."

As I was saying the words, the nurse indicated a pump that was dangling at the side of the bed. She showed me how to operate it, releasing a controlled amount of morphine into the catheter in my arm.

"You should experience the effects within the next few minutes," she explained in a matter-of-fact tone. "It will help you to feel more comfortable. You must try to eat something too. Tomorrow we'll need to get you up and walking." She then proceeded to tell me about a seventy-year-old man, further down the ward, who also had undergone a nephrectomy. His operation had been carried out after mine, but he was already able to get out of bed unaided.

I looked at her as though she must be joking. I could barely sit upright. At that moment, the simple act of walking seemed so impossible that she might just as well have suggested that I take part in an Ironman triathlon!

"Come now, Mr. Trochon," she said briskly, in response to my pained expression. "You're young and strong. You have to push yourself a bit ..." She wheeled a cart toward the bed and indicated a tray of food. "Have a bite to eat. It will help you to regain your strength."

With that, she bustled out of the room. Alone again and with the pain subsiding a little as the morphine kicked in, I warily lifted one of the metal lids covering the dishes on the tray. The smell of some kind of congealed sauce hit my nostrils and immediately made me feel nauseated. I was unable to ascertain whether the brownish sludge was covering lumps of chicken or pork. I was pretty certain that any possible nutrients had been blitzed out of the concoction when it was heated up in the microwave. This was my first encounter with hospital food, and it appeared that the rumors were true. Rejecting the offending dish, I instead managed to swallow a few spoonfuls of yogurt and slices of apple.

Any dignity that I'd had when entering the hospital had long since been stripped from me together with my clothing. Apart from the flimsy, open-backed hospital gown, my legs were also encased up to above the knee in compression stockings. This was definitely not a good look and only succeeded in making me appear even more fragile and vulnerable. Being largely unable to eat served to heighten this impression.

The next two days were punctuated by visits from various members of the team on duty. Things were not going well. The nurses seemed convinced that I was not making sufficient effort in my recovery. They were not happy that I was leaving most of my food untouched, despite the fact that I told them my stomach was hurting. The truth was I felt queasy whenever I tried to swallow anything more substantial than soup. Another major bone of contention was my apparent inability to even get out of bed to walk around the room without help. My energy seemed to quite literally be draining away with every hour that passed. At one point I had two nurses on either side of me, trying to force me to put one foot in front of the other. I just couldn't do it. My head spinning, I saw black dots in front of my eyes, and my body crumpled back onto the bed with every pitiful attempt.

My progress was repeatedly compared to that of the older man a few rooms down. This superhuman septuagenarian was now able to walk down the corridor to shower unaided, barely two days after his operation. I didn't know what was happening to me, but my pain had become so great that even the morphine didn't have much of an impact. I felt increasingly weak and dizzy.

It was only on day three that Doctor Landé was called in to re-examine me. He had, of course, seen me on his daily rounds, but his visits had lasted no more than a few minutes due to the number of other patients awaiting his care. As a result, he had relied upon the on-duty nurses to inform him of any cause for concern. By now my skin color had changed to a morgue-like pallor, and I was having trouble responding to questions. I felt jumpy and unable to concentrate. Taking one look at me, the doctor immediately ordered blood tests and a bedside ultrasound examination. The test results revealed that my red blood cell count had plummeted. My blood pressure was also abnormally low, which explained my light-headedness. The ultrasound revealed substantial internal bleeding that had amassed around the area of my operation and was spreading throughout my abdomen. The cause was traced back to the anti-inflammatory tablets I had been given as painkillers. It seemed that I'd had a bad reaction, to put it mildly. (If not dealt with rapidly, internal bleeding can lead to organ failure and death. I'm glad I did not discover this sobering fact until later.)

Shortly after informing me of the diagnosis, I heard my doctor reprimand the nursing staff in the corridor with scalding language. I heard him say that they should be more attentive to individual patients' needs and not be so quick to make comparisons between cases.

I am not interested in apportioning any blame. I have witnessed how hard all of the nursing staff work. Their job is often a thankless one that involves tough physical labor, long hours, and low pay. Internal bleeding is not easy to detect. Unlike a cut on the body, which is evident to the naked eye, the initial signs may be mistaken for less serious conditions, most of which are to be expected after major surgery. Whatever the cause and whoever might be responsible, I just felt relieved that I was now going to be looked after.

Everything then happened quickly. The main hospital had sent blood via an emergency service. Within an hour, I was hooked to a machine and undergoing a transfusion. It was a strange experience, one that made me feel almost "high" due to the oxygenated life source entering my body. It was not unlike that rush of euphoria I felt when surfing, when I'd ride a final fantastic wave after hours of being battered incessantly by the ocean. I tried not to look at the red fluid flowing through the tube into my veins. Being a bit of a germaphobe, I couldn't help but feel a little weird about someone else's blood circulating through me.

I had plenty of time to reflect upon my situation because the seven units of blood I received took several hours to transfuse. Much of the day and night, I again drifted fitfully in and out of sleep. Having been taken off the painkillers, the hemorrhaging stopped, and I was out of any immediate danger. My pain also lessened, despite the morphine being reduced. I even awoke with a bit of an appetite once the transfusion had finished.

As I started to regain strength, I began to do the things that the nurses had expected of me a few days previously. I was able to shuffle to the bathroom unaided. I managed to shave and transform the grizzly faced old man, who had grimaced at me from the bathroom mirror, back to one approaching my normal visage. A neon strip light never did anyone any favors, but I nevertheless looked as though I had aged by at least a decade in just a few days. My eyes were gaunt, my skin was sallow and my previously well-defined arms looked scrawny and flaccid — like those of a heroin addict, a fact not mitigated by the numerous injection marks on the insides of my wrists.

I still couldn't bring myself to look at the zone of the operation itself. I no longer had a drainage tube protruding from my body, and the small incision through which it had been inserted had been neatly stitched up. However, the bandage covering what used to be the area of my kidney was frighteningly large. It was not until I was ready to leave the hospital that the bandage and stitches were finally removed. The angry-looking scar was certainly impressive at eighteen centimeters in length. Doctor Landé had done as I'd asked ... he had left me resembling a victim of a shark attack. Indeed, this story seemed at the time to be more heroic than that of a cancer patient.

Although I had yet to fully appreciate that a battle with cancer is, indeed, a heroic journey, something had clicked into place within me. Having almost died twice ... once from the cancer and once from internal bleeding, I had found a renewed will to survive. I also realized I needed to take matters more into my own hands. The medical professionals do an amazing job, but they are only human. Sometimes we have to listen to our intuition and undertake our own research into what is best for our health. And that's precisely what I decided to do.

CHAPTER 4

White Poison

"The prime cause of cancer is the replacement
of the respiration of oxygen in normal body cells
by a fermentation of sugar."

*~Otto H. Warburg, German physiologist,
medical doctor, and Nobel laureate*

I HAD PLENTY OF TIME to ponder my fate over the next few
days since my stay in the hospital had been prolonged by the
internal bleeding. Restless and bored, I began to peruse the
magazines and novels that friends had left for me. Nothing
really grabbed my attention. Reading was difficult at first, on
account of my weakened eyesight. Nevertheless, my thirst for
knowledge led me to persevere.

To be honest, I've never really been interested in reading fiction. I often find it slow and boring, with far too many adjectives and phrases describing scenery, as well as conversations that have never taken place and with characters to whom I can't relate. However, I can happily read and re-read a work of non-fiction from cover to cover if it relates to a specific subject that I'm curious to know more about. Among the pile of literature, one book in particular piqued my curiosity. Entitled *Guérir le stress, l'anxieté et la dépression* (later published in English as *Healing Without Freud or Prozac*), it was written by French neuroscientist David Servan-Schreiber. The book had been a gift from my mum when she and Dad visited me in the hospital on the day following my operation.

Even now, I feel a little sad when I remember my small, gray-haired mum as she sat perched like a frail and anxious bird at the side of my hospital bed. She was already starting to show the signs of arthritis that would later lead to her becoming severely handicapped and dependent upon other people.

My mum had always been active, rushing from one place to the other, as she juggled caring for her three children and attending a wide range of social activities. Above all she had loved her garden and could name all the trees and flowers that flourished in it. Back then it would have been unthinkable to imagine her confined to an apartment, unable to walk without the aid of her walker, her *chariot*, as she called it. Perhaps it is just as well that we can't see into the future.

I knew that Mum had agonized at the breakdown of my marriage. Nobody in my family had ever gotten a divorce.

Visiting me in the hospital, she suffered again on account of my cancer diagnosis. I think that one of the worst things imaginable for any parent is to see their child seriously ill. My mum would have done anything to stop my pain. She had undergone so much hardship in her own lifetime and had little concern for herself.

Mum, Michèle Trochon née Mercier, spent her young years in Tunisia, where her father, Roger Pierre Mercier, was a high-ranking officer in the French army. My grandfather later went on to become a famous member of the *Maquis*, the French resistance who fought against the Nazis during World War II. Fighting under the code name "Maxime," he was captured by the Germans and murdered in the killing center housed in Hartheim Castle, a subcamp of the notorious Mauthausen concentration camp in Austria. Roger Pierre was posthumously distinguished, among other accolades, with the *Légion d'Honneur*. Established in 1802 by Napoleon Bonaparte and retained by all later French governments and regimes, the *Légion d'Honneur* is France's highest military and civilian medal.

Photographs from his youth show that I bear a striking resemblance to my grandfather. It's a fact that makes me proud, since I have grown up on the stories of his heroism, idolizing the man I never met. I strive to live up to his memory and hope that my children will be equally proud of me.

The book that Mum left me was geared at overcoming depression in the face of life's adversities. More than the actual book, what intrigued me was its author.

Neurosurgeon Servan-Schreiber had himself been diagnosed with a brain tumor in 1991. The fact that he was still around to tell the tale gave me a huge boost. I wanted to know more about this remarkable physician and his approach to health.

Following conventional treatment, Servan-Schreiber had suffered a relapse and subsequently had undergone surgery and chemotherapy. He then asked his oncologist for advice on how to lead a healthy, cancer-free life. At the time, his physician, a highly reputed medical professional, told him, "Lead your life normally. We'll do CAT scans at regular intervals, and if your tumor comes back, we'll detect it early."

Servan-Schreiber rejected this wait-and-see approach. Instead, he went in search of alternative treatments that could also serve to prevent cancer in the first place. His research led him to the conclusion that, while we all have potential cancer cells lying dormant within us, each of us also has a body designed to fight the process of tumor development. Each one of us can draw upon our body's natural defenses. Servan-Schreiber did not advocate rejecting conventional Western medicine, such as surgery, chemotherapy, radiotherapy and immunotherapy. However, he strongly believed that patients could help these treatments to be more effective by boosting their immunity and eliminating certain toxins from the environment, adopting an anti-cancer diet, seeking emotional balance, and getting sufficient exercise.

Servan-Schreiber later wrote, "Being a physician and scientist is no protection from getting cancer. But it allowed me to dig deeply into the medical and scientific literature in search of ways to live longer than the few years I was expected to survive."

Following Servan-Schreiber's example, I, too, began to dig deeper while I was still in the hospital. As a result of my internet research, I came across another name that would prove to have a major impact on me—that of German biologist Otto Heinrich Warburg, the pioneering scientist who investigated the metabolism of tumors and the respiration of cells, particularly cancer cells.

After receiving forty-six Nobel Prize nominations over nine years, Warburg's work was finally acknowledged, in 1931, with the Nobel Prize in Physiology for his discovery that the metabolism of malignant tumors is largely dependent on glucose consumption. In other words, sugar feeds tumors.

Ironically, it seems that Adolf Hitler, a man who was responsible for so much death and destruction, had his part to play in what we now know about cancer and its development. Hitler was said to be terrified of cancer. On May 23, 1935, he underwent surgery to remove a polyp growing on his larynx. He also suffered with indigestion and flatulence, which led him to believe he had both throat and stomach cancer, neither of which proved to be the case. However, it was this paranoia that led to the authorization of Warburg's ongoing research into the primary cause of cancer and its potential reversal. It was largely thanks to this research that Warburg was spared the horrific fate of so many of his compatriots.

Born to a Protestant mother and a Jewish father, who later converted to Protestantism, Warburg was considered by the Nazis as a *Mischling* or half-Jew. In September 1942, however, he submitted an official request for equal status (*Gleichstellung*) with Germans, which was granted.

The scientist went on to discover that the primary cause of cancer is oxygen deficiency brought about by toxicity and other secondary conditions in the body. If deprived of 35 percent of its oxygen needs, he found that a cell would turn cancerous within forty-eight hours. Cancer cells, he discovered, are generated when the respiration of oxygen in normal body cells is replaced by a fermentation of sugar. Warburg was able to demonstrate that cancer cells could be brought back to a healthy state by adding a higher concentration of oxygen.

His Jewish heritage notwithstanding, Warburg was acknowledged as Hitler's authority on cancer and was undoubtedly protected by the *Fuehrer* himself. Despite being removed from his position in 1941 by the Nazi hierarchy, after he made critical comments about the regime, Warburg resumed his cancer research a few weeks later at the personal order from Hitler's Chancellery.

Warburg's research, today referred to as the Warburg Effect, was largely dismissed by scientists and researchers for decades. Only in fairly recent times has his research been acknowledged for the groundbreaking work that it was. Unfortunately, this realization has come far too late, since refined sugar is now an additive in most processed foods. I've come to see it as "white poison," because it is killing us.

The words of both Servan-Schreiber and the work of Otto

Warburg resonated with me, and I decided to set off on my own anti-cancer journey.

I felt sick to my stomach as I thought back to the sugary delights that I used to indulge in over the course of my job as an airline pilot. During the often tedious transfer between airport and hotel, it was a tradition among crews to share sweets and boxes of chocolates given to them by grateful passengers. It helped relieve the boredom and fatigue after a long flight. Now I realize that I was feeding my growing tumor at the same time.

I fervently hoped it wasn't too late for me to reverse the damage. The first thing I did was to cut sugar from my diet— out went the pastries, butter-laden croissants and baguettes, desserts and sweet treats, as well as white rice and pasta. I knew it wasn't going to be easy, especially living in a country renowned for its gastronomic delights. But I also knew that, if I wanted to survive, I had no choice.

The remainder of my time in the hospital, I did rehab exercises to regain my strength, which came back a little more each day. The stronger I became, the more my frustration grew at not being able to support the South African team in the rugby tournament. I really felt that I'd been kicked when I was down, since the tournament had been the one beacon of light on an otherwise bleak landscape that was my existence back then.

The email sent by South Africa's Butch Watson-Smith had spread the word of my illness far and wide. Messages from my rugby-player friends flooded my inbox. Friends like Brent Russell, nicknamed "Pocket Rocket" due to his diminutive size and awesome speed; Maurius Joubert, who was only the second Springbok in history (after Ray Mordt in 1981) to score a hat-trick of tries (goals) against New Zealand's All Blacks; and Breyton Paulse, who went on to become the famous defender who stopped the previously thought unstoppable New Zealand "juggernaut" Jonah Lomu from ever scoring a try against the Springboks. I felt a powerful outpouring of love from these incredible young players, and it strengthened my renewed will to live.

Perhaps one of the most touching messages came from the Under-19 team manager, Mervin Green. We had met for the first time some three months earlier when Mervin came to Paris to discuss arrangements for the forthcoming tournament. Over those three days, we developed a real friendship and shared stories about our lives, to the point that he seemed like a family member, a brother almost, since I was even able to confide in him about my marital problems.

Mervin is a soft-spoken man, stocky in stature and with conker-brown skin. He belongs to a multiracial ethnic group referred to as "Coloureds." While seen as a derogatory term outside South Africa, there it is used to denote people who have ancestry from more than one of the various populations inhabiting the region, including Khoisan, Bantu, Afrikaner, English, Austronesian, East Asian or South Asian. Resulting from this melting pot of ethnicities is a people with a variety of physical features, differences that often are apparent between members of the same family. The prevalent language of Coloureds is Afrikaans, a language imported by the Dutch, who were among the first colonists in the country along with the French and Germans. English is also widely spoken.

Like many South Africans, and especially those of the Coloured community, Mervin is a religious man and had practiced as a minister in his younger years. I felt at ease in his company from the moment I met him. Mervin had been distressed to hear that I was in the hospital and wanted me to know how much I was missed. At that point I had been hospitalized for more than two weeks, and the games were already well underway. I had been following the progress of "my boys" on local TV and knew that they were through to the semi-finals, which would be held the following week. So when Mervin told me that everyone was waiting for me to attend the game, I knew that he was being sincere and not just trying to make me feel better.

Despite the idea being totally unreasonable, given my condition at that time, and also going against the advice of my doctor, I also knew that I would do whatever it would take to get me there ... I would be at that game!

CHAPTER 5

United We Shall Stand

MATCH DAY.

"Laughter is the best medicine" may be an old cliché, but it is one that holds a great deal of truth. Regardless of the pain I was in, the thought of attending the rugby tournament and laughing with my rugby friends is what got me through those difficult first days post-hospital. Ever since my release, I'd kept my blazer, shirt and tie hanging on the back of the bedroom door on prominent display so that I could will myself to be fit enough for the big day.

The morning of the semi-final of the Under-19 World Cup tournament, my fingers trembled as I knotted my tie, and when I eased my left arm into the blazer, it sent a jolt of pain down my side. I would have been more comfortable in a Springboks jersey and jeans, but I felt it important to show my respect to the team management after I'd received so many messages of support.

I hadn't shared with my doctor my intention to attend the tournament, in which the country of my heart, South Africa, would be pitted against France, the country of my birth. Many people find it strange that, although I carry a French passport, I am so passionate about South Africa, and especially its rugby team. Maybe it's because I spent the first two years of my life on the island of Madagascar, where my dad was stationed at the time. Perhaps it's on account of my early experience as a commercial pilot on seven-seater planes in Abidjan, economic capital of the Ivory Coast. Or the countless times I accompanied my dad to South Africa, Zimbabwe and other African countries when I was younger. I believe all of these experiences left an imprint on me to the extent that part of my soul lives in Africa.

The Under-19 league comprised the most promising up-and-comers on their way to the big leagues of professional international rugby. Some people might dismiss junior rugby as inconsequential, but I have always loved it. I am naturally an educator, having started to teach aviation shortly after getting my wings. During my obligatory military service, I was sent to Algeria, where I worked as a flight instructor at the national school for student pilots. I have continued to instruct throughout my aviation career. And, of course, I have taught my own children to surf and to play rugby. It is always such a pleasure to teach kids.

Getting to know the young players in the Under-19 tournament was a privilege. From the beginning, they called me
"Uncle" as a sign of respect and always listened to what I
had to say, eager to learn about life. As time went on, I have
loved watching them as they progress throughout their rugby
careers, many becoming Springboks.

I had ignored my doctor's advice to take it easy, and I
feared that if he knew my plans, he might send the "health
police" around to strap me to my bed! But, having missed out
on my chance to be a liaison officer for the tournament, there
was no way that I would forego attending this match.

Accompanying me to the stadium were two generous
friends with whom I had been staying ever since leaving the
hospital. Their spare room was a temporary measure, but I
was in no shape to go back to the remote farmhouse in which
I had been living. Anyway, I had no interest in returning to
that gloomy place. I was ready to make a fresh start, just as
soon as I was well enough to do so.

On the way to the stadium, we passed coachloads of
supporters, all dressed in their teams' colors and vigorously
waving flags through the windows as they hooted their horns
and shouted good-natured taunts to rival fans. This was the
world that I knew and loved, having been part of it since 1999,
when I first got involved with South Africa's national team. To
be honest, my voluntary liaison officer role was (and still is) a
real highlight of my year, whenever the Springboks or "Baby
Boks" (as the juniors in the Under-19 league are known) play
in France. It felt so good to be back.

In truth, I knew it was madness for me to attend such a large sporting event. I had been out of the hospital for a little over a week and still found it exhausting to walk more than a few meters. Yet, my determination was stronger than the pain. These were my very first steps into the outside world.

My head was spinning and my body felt like I'd done a few rounds with Mike Tyson. As we made our way through the throng of boisterous fans, my friends were at my side, shielding me against any unintentional jolts. I advanced slowly, my gait awkward and wobbly. I had to stop every five to ten minutes to catch my breath. The extensive blood loss I'd suffered in the hospital had delayed my overall recovery. Nevertheless, as I approached the stairs to the stands, I replayed the scalding words of the nurse in my head, telling me that I had to make an effort to walk. Now I was showing her. I was walking.

My progress might be slow, I thought, *but I've come on a challenging journey to get here, and I am going to take my place, however long it takes.*

We made our way straight to the *tribune d'honneur*, which was reserved for the management, local dignitaries and VIPs. From a few yards away, I saw Mervin Green anxiously looking out for me at the entrance to the tribune. He was easy to spot on account of his official green blazer. We hugged each other with the familiarity of brothers. I sensed that he was being careful not to exert pressure on my fragile body. Supporting my weight, he walked with me up the remaining stairs and eased me into the seat next to his.

It was then that I saw Mervin's eyes had filled with tears, his skin glistening as one or two had escaped and left tracks down his plump cheeks. I could tell that he was shocked at my dramatically changed appearance. Just three months earlier, when Mervin and I had first met, I had been running all over the city with him, taking him from venue to venue in preparation for the tournament. My energy had been boundless, like an over-eager puppy. Now my own skin had lost its sun-tanned, healthy glow, the result of so many hours in the cockpit and flights to exotic destinations. Perhaps it was my imagination, but my hair also seemed to have changed color, with more strands of silvery gray and white than before the operation.

As I listened to the crowd's chanting and observed fathers and sons taking their seats in excited anticipation of the game, I couldn't help thinking about my own son and how I wished he was there with me. I had first taken him to see a game in South Africa when he was around five years old. Jeff had his own Springboks rugby jersey, which he would proudly wear to look like a "mini me."

It wasn't long into the game before my natural instincts took over. Momentarily forgetting my physical state, I screamed encouragement to the Boks. After all I'd been through, I was just so elated to be there. I wanted my rugby family to know that I was back and that my blood was still green, just as Butch had said. I soon regretted this outburst of enthusiasm, since my fragile nerve endings were in the process of rebuilding after the operation. The pain felt like an electric current surging throughout my body. I protectively put my hand to the area from which my kidney had been removed. It served as a powerful reminder that my recovery would require time and patience. I spent the rest of the game watching with silent admiration, keeping my passion in check.

When the final whistle of the semi-final was blown, South Africa emerged victorious against France with a score of 20–15. The match had been a tense one, with both teams playing a tight game. Naturally, the French had the advantage of being on home ground with the support of local fans. South Africa's victory was therefore even sweeter, since most of these young players were unaccompanied by family and had traveled outside their country for the first time.

Despite my delight at the result, I was drained of energy and ready to retreat back to my friends' place. It had been chilly in the stands, with an unrelenting dampness that ate into my bones. Having lost so much weight during my time in the hospital, I had very little padding to protect me from the cold. That night, I fell into bed, exhausted but happy.

Four days later, I returned to watch the boys play the final against New Zealand's Baby Blacks. I was even more excited for this game, since South Africa and New Zealand are famous rivals in the world of rugby.

I was again given a place of honor in the stands. Seated right at the top, on a bench a few rows behind me, was the team coach, Eugene Eloff (or Loffie, as he is known by his friends). A former colonel and parachutist in the South African infantry, he had a reputation as a guy who cared deeply about every player on his team. Despite being focused on the forthcoming match, Loffie came down to greet me and to thank me personally for preparing everything ahead of the tournament. He had heard about my sudden illness and was relieved to see me at the game.

Shortly before the game was to start, the French match commentator came over to Mervin and asked him for help in pronouncing some of the South African names. Names such as *Mkokeli, Van der Westhuizen,* and *Mxoli* do not exactly roll off a French speaker's tongue. Mervin turned to me and said, "Would you like to do it for us?"

Not needing to be asked twice, I eagerly accepted. I hadn't been able to fulfill my role as liaison officer, but at least now I had some small way of contributing to the cause.

A few minutes later, I'd moved to a seat at the press table and was talking about the South African players over the microphone to the stadium audience, as naturally as if I were making an announcement to my passengers mid-flight. To look at me in that moment, nobody would have imagined that, just a couple of weeks previously, I'd been fighting for my life. I guess I got swept up in the euphoria of the atmosphere because, during those few minutes, I felt better than ever.

The final was heralded by much fanfare and a rousing rendition of the South African national anthem. I'll admit to being a little ashamed that I don't know all of the words to France's *Marseillaise*, but I am proud to say that I can sing *Nkosi Sikelel' iAfrika* off by heart. The lyrics truly represent the "rainbow nation" by employing five of the country's most widely spoken languages, namely Xhosa, Zulu, Sesotho, Afrikaans and English. The English verse is as follows:

> *Sounds the call to come together,*
> *And united we shall stand,*
> *Let us live and strive for freedom,*
> *In South Africa our land!*

True to this sentiment, the boys played a strong game against their mighty opponents. One moment in particular has stuck with me ever since. I witnessed the smallest guy on the field, Anwell September, a winger who went by the nickname of *Sharky*, receive a hammering from his New Zealand opponent, a giant called Hosea Gear, who thundered down the pitch at him like an unstoppable freight train.

Things looked grim for the South African team. We had fallen behind and drastic action was needed. So, at halftime, Loffie went down into the changing rooms and gave the team a pep talk. I don't know what he said, but he has since told me that a lot of his rugby coaching skills were drawn from his time spent in the military.

"I had to keep my soldiers motivated, to keep them alive, to keep them safe and well-fed," he later explained. "It's not dissimilar to rugby, where it's about getting a team together, preparing them well for battle, going into battle on the ground and making sure that everyone comes back alive."

Whatever Loffie said to the team that day, little *Sharky* came back a changed man. He'd tripled his energy and pivoted to such an aggressive approach that his Kiwi counterpart now appeared afraid to take him on. Young Anwell's energy was matched by all of the Baby Boks, who seemed to have a newfound determination to win. After some tense final minutes, they succeeded in scraping victory from their old adversaries with a score of 22–18.

Just before going up to collect their cup and individual medals, the boys huddled together in a circle. Their voices rang out in unison, singing *Shosholoza* with an unbridled joy and purity that came from within their souls. The song has deep roots in South African culture. Originally sung by tribes of all-male African workers digging for gold in the mines, it comprises a mix of Zulu and Ndebele words. *Shosholoza* itself literally means *to go forward* or *make way for the next man* in Ndebele. A sign of solidarity, *Shosholoza* has particular significance since former South African president, Nelson Mandela, has described how he sang it while working during his imprisonment on Robben Island.

Nowadays the song also has a deeper meaning because it was officially introduced to the sport of rugby at the legendary 1995 World Cup at Ellis Park Stadium in Johannesburg, South Africa, just one year after Nelson Mandela had been sworn in as the country's first black president. The host nation's Springboks again faced their rivals, the All Blacks. At the time, the Springboks had just one non-white player, Chester Williams, and black South Africans hated the team for many reasons, seeing their green jerseys as symbols of apartheid repression. Nevertheless, Mandela convinced the nation to pull together as one and stand behind the Springboks.

As an incredible gesture of solidarity in a country still tending its wounds from the struggles of apartheid, Mandela appeared on the field at the start of the match wearing a Springboks jersey. The 65,000-strong crowd initially was stunned into silence, which was then broken by chants of "Nelson! Nelson! Nelson!" South Africa went on to win the game, 15 to 12, and South Africans of all colors celebrated the victory, loudly singing *Shosholoza* in honor of Nelson Mandela and the momentousness of the occasion.

As Mandela himself said, "Sport has the power to change the world. It has the power to inspire. It has the power to unite people in a way that little else does." The words of *Shosholoza* also had special significance for me back then. I, too, was part of a team. I was part of this team of passionate young sportsmen, and also the team of my airline colleagues at Air France. Buoyed by my rugby team's win, I felt a renewed determination to get back into the cockpit. Just like the little guy on the right wing, I would redouble my efforts to return to good health and regain my license.

That night the boys headed into Paris to celebrate their victory at the city's only South African bar, the legendary *Pomme d'Eve*, which was (and still is, as of this writing) owned by my good friend George, a Greek South African. Set in the iconic *Quartier Latin* of Paris, the bar is housed in a magnificent gothic cellar dating back to the twelfth century. It used to be part of Saint Geneviève's Abbey, providing a striking contrast to its present-day use.

How I would have loved to join the team as they drank their victory bottles of Windhoek and Castle lager, accompanied by plenty of *biltong* and *boerewors*, no doubt reliving the game minute-by-minute, try-by-try.

I couldn't help but feel a sense of disappointment at missing out on the celebrations. Indeed, it reminded me of being a little kid who was too sick to attend a friend's birthday party. But I knew that I needed to focus on getting well. I was involved in a bigger game and had to do what I needed to do, so I could fly again. At that moment, I needed to be quiet and rest, to gather my energy and concentrate my thoughts on healing. My own victory was within reach if I played by the rules.

CHAPTER 6

Business as Usual

OUTSTRETCHED BELOW ME lay the Massif des Maures, with its dense forests of chestnut and cork oak trees interlaced with scorched earth and resilient scrubland. The hilly landscape is one of necessary resistance, forced to hold its own when blistering temperatures give way to the relentless howling of the Mistral, a violent wind that often lasts several days. Scattered here and there, clinging to the hilltops, medieval villages of time-worn stone emitted a warm glow in the afternoon sunshine. As the plane descended, I could make out orchards of gnarled olive trees, as well as umbrella pines, their flat-topped canopies bent at an angle after incessant battering by the elements. And then, just as my eyes had grown accustomed to the earthy palette of greens and browns, it was gone, replaced by the bluest of blues that can only be the Mediterranean Sea.

Here, we took a right turn and headed out over the ocean, opening up a spectacular vista of the glittering Côte d'Azur. I couldn't have asked for a better welcome. My parents had moved to the military port of Toulon after my father retired, so in a sense I was coming home whenever I landed in the city's nearby airport of Hyères. It felt good to return to this familiar part of the world, especially after the journey that I'd been on to get here. This time I was coming to collect my kids, who had been staying with their grandparents. I eagerly anticipated the reunion ahead.

The scenery of the French Riviera never fails to take my breath away. From an altitude of 1,500 feet, it still bears the vestiges of 1950s postcard glamor. Sophisticated villas decorate the cliff tops like strings of shiny pearls, silent hosts to many a celluloid star of that golden age, while showy yachts glide through the waters as effortlessly as oil paint spread on canvas. For a moment, I allowed myself to soak it all up, just grateful to be alive.

Nevertheless, a split second later, my mind returned to more serious matters. "Cabin crew, prepare for landing," I spoke into the passenger address system. I was almost surprised to hear myself utter these familiar words, yet, there was no doubt about it ... I was back in business!

Looping the A320 back toward the mainland for the final approach, I reveled in the sheer joy of sitting in the cockpit again. It's where I belong. It's in my blood, just as it was in my father's before me.

"This is the best office in the world!" Dad would say. And, as I looked down at the shimmering ocean beneath me, I couldn't help but agree. I also couldn't wait to see him and my mum after landing—they'd been so supportive throughout my ordeal. But most of all, I was excited about seeing my kids and flying them back to Paris with me.

This was my first flight after regaining my license following my bout with kidney cancer. No one expected me to be back in the hot seat just four and a half months after my operation.

Part of the training process to regain one's license is to "fly" a plane using a simulator, which had been tough to begin with. After being sick, it was natural that I would lose some confidence, but my surety quickly returned when I went through the motions of flying. Deep down, I always knew that I would make it. I only had to think back to my close brush with death to make me even more determined to succeed. That late August flight was jam-packed with happy tourists eager to roast themselves in the sunshine on the golden sands of the South of France. Plenty of locals were on board too. The latter were easy to recognize on account of their deep tans, sun-bleached hair, and flashy gold jewelry. The residents of southern France also tend to wear colorful clothing throughout the year, setting them apart from the more muted style of Parisians.

The landing that day was a beauty. A little while before making the final approach, I pointed out the breathtaking spectacle of the coastline to my passengers. Having been away for a bit, it felt to me like I was seeing it with fresh eyes. I wanted everyone to share in my elation at being given a second chance at life. It was all I could do to refrain from shouting it out over the passenger address system, but I managed to stop myself and kept my tone steady. The plane then descended further. The radio altimeter was triggered in the cockpit, its robotic voice calling out the heights until landing:

"1000 ... 500, 400, 300 ... approaching minimums, 100, 50, 40 ..."

I fixed my attention on the landing strip in front of me and navigated the silver bird to a smooth touchdown. My co-pilot knew it was my first flight in a while. He looked at me with a big smile on his face and gave me the thumbs-up. Yep, it was good to be back!

Once all passengers had disembarked, I filled out the necessary paperwork and then hurried to the terminal. It was a fairly quick turnaround that day, but I still had time for a brief chat with Mum and Dad. I hadn't seen them since being hospitalized, so it was going to be a special reunion for all of us. Before entering the building, I made sure to place my Air France cap squarely on my head. I have always worn my uniform with pride, but at that moment it symbolized so much more than just my career. I had fought so hard to wear it again. In this knowledge, I was determined to walk tall, my head held high.

Mum and Dad were waiting at the arrival gate, standing side by side, my mum's arm linked through my dad's. This was both a gesture of love and one of a practical nature, since

Mum struggled to stand for too long. It's strange to see your parents aging. Growing up, you only ever consider them to be old, and yet, when you become a parent yourself, you realize how young they were when they tried to guide you along life's bumpy path.

One of my favorite photos of my dad shows him in the cockpit of a DC-10 in the years approaching his retirement. In it, he has the glamor of a fifties Hollywood star, his startling blue eyes recalling those of the legendary Paul Newman. No wonder so many of the older cabin crew members still remember my dad today, often asking me if he and I are related when they see my name on the crew list. Both he and my mum experienced the glory days of early aviation. Mum worked as a hostess before we kids were born. It's how she and Dad met. Mum was always petite and athletic. A real classic beauty in her day. It pained me to see her gradually losing strength in the limbs that used to so easily take command of a tennis court.

I caught a glimpse of my kids, who were hiding behind my parents, waiting to spring out at me. Like two tightly wound-up clockwork monkeys, they came running toward me with their limbs flailing wildly as they threw themselves into my own outstretched arms. We embraced tightly, forming an unbreakable unit once more. I then looked over at my parents and was equally overwhelmed to see the light of happiness and love shining in their eyes.

My dad, not given to shows of emotion, approached and patted me firmly on the back.

"You're looking good, *mon Coco*."

I smiled to hear him adopt the pet name that he used to call me as a child. There was a touching tenderness to it, underlining the strength of our bond. I am their *aîné*, their firstborn.

Looking at my dad on that day, he could best be described as portly. Protruding beneath his favorite leather vest, its front suede panels shiny with wear, a familiar blue checked shirt could be seen stretched across his stomach. This was the uniform that my dad had adopted in his retirement. His trusty pipe also peeped coyly from a top pocket. A smoker for much of his adult years, he was battling to give up the deadly pleasure. Judging by his expanding waistline, he was overcompensating with sweet treats and generous glasses of red wine. But the pipe was still there as some kind of safety mechanism. It comforted him to feel its presence, even unlit.

At times my father had been severe with me, since I often had to act as head of the household when he was away on flights. In those days he could be away for a few weeks at a time, making it difficult for him to reassert his authority upon returning to the family home. I can remember him chasing me around our garden when, as an awkward adolescent, I answered back. He didn't always catch me, but I would get a firm spank when he did. It was his way of showing me who was boss, even if he was often absent. But I never really doubted it. Dad was always my hero—an airline captain who took me up in the cockpit when I was just two years old. From the word go, I was entranced by the incredible sights of flying and marveled at my father's focus, his ease in the hot seat and his mastery of aviation. Over the years, I had often wondered if my own children would be drawn to this enchanting world as I had been. As it turns out, Kelly is the one who loves to be around planes whenever she can.

Mum reached up to stroke my cheek. Sensing her need, Jeff and Kelly spontaneously released their grip to make room for their grandmother to put her arms around me. I gently kissed her forehead, aware that her eyes were welling up with tears. She, too, is of the generation that doesn't easily show their feelings. Once you've experienced such grief at an early age, as Mum did when her father was murdered as a prisoner of war, you become immune to many of life's difficulties, learning to "grin and bear it." And yet I know how much she suffered when I was ill. I saw it in her eyes when she visited me in the hospital, afraid that her eldest son would die before her.

"I love you, Mum," I whispered, hugging her close and combing my fingers through her soft gray hair. She felt so fragile, and yet I knew that she was probably the most resilient of us all.

"It's all good. I'm here and I'm feeling great," I reassured her.

Mum smiled back at me, her relief evident.

Our time together was brief, but it had boosted my morale to see my parents and to show them that I was doing well. Not only had I come back fighting from my brush with cancer, but I was now coping with my divorce. Life goes on.

I prepared to head back to the plane, feeling happy in the knowledge that Jeff and Kelly would be with me on the return flight. Unfortunately, this one was going to be completely full, but I had been able to assign them jump seats. My happiness was temporarily clouded upon overhearing an off-duty member of the cabin crew complaining about youngsters being given such privileges. He was addressing a small group of Air France employees who had been on standby for my flight, but who now would have to wait for a later one. As captain, I get to decide who will sit in the jump seats, and there was no way I was going to leave my children behind that day. I had been looking forward to that flight with them ever since I got my wings back.

I reminded the person in question of my authority. I informed him that it was my first flight after battling cancer. Perhaps it would serve as a lesson to not judge the actions of others until you have walked in their shoes. For his sake, I hope he never has to.

Accompanied by my children, I strode back out onto the tarmac toward my plane. I momentarily got the kids to pose on the steps, and I took a couple of snapshots before they clambered inside. (Those same photos now take pride of place on the desk in my office, a poignant reminder of how far I have come.) The children joined me in the cockpit and sat quietly strapped into their jump seats while I commenced the flight preparations. They have been flying with me since they were very young, so they know the routine. My co-pilot then joined me, and we got into the so-called "sterile" cockpit mode. This procedure protects a cockpit for takeoff and landing. It basically means that there is no communication between those in the cockpit and those beyond the cockpit door. Until a certain altitude is reached, there is also no verbal exchange in the cockpit itself, other than that relating to the strict flight procedures.

Just as we were about to take off, I glanced back toward the airport and to the cluster of cars parked just outside it. I knew that somewhere out there, among the vehicles of plane spotters, sat my mum and dad. They had said that they would stay and watch me take off. I felt both reassured and proud to know that they were there for me. Just as they always had been, and just as I would always be there for my own children.

With that, I put the throttle forward into the takeoff position. The plane accelerated down the runway, rotated and ascended into the blue horizon, where the ocean merged with the sky.

CHAPTER 7

Together We Are an Ocean

"Individually, we are one drop.
Together, we are an ocean."

~Ryunosuke Satoro, Japanese poet

MEMORIES OF MY CHILDHOOD are infused with the heady scents of vanilla, tiaré blossom and coconut. They are the scents of Tahiti, which is where I spent my early years. Even today, if I close my eyes, I can still picture my dad lying in a hammock in our tropical, flower-filled garden, the island of Moorea just visible in the distance. I can almost hear the sounds of waves crashing onto the sandy beach just beyond our typical wooden house, with its thatched roof and rustic bamboo shutters. As childhoods go, it was idyllic. We moved to the island from Madagascar when I was around three years old.

My dad was employed as a pilot for a company called RAI (Reseau Aerian Interinsulaire), later to become Air Tahiti. At the time, he flew Bermudas, four-engine seaplanes, to other islands in French Polynesia, including Bora Bora and the Marquesas. He then had the honor of being the first pilot to open the route between Tahiti and Rangiroa, the largest atoll in the Pacific. Rangiroa was a crucial hub connecting the smaller islands and had previously only been accessible by boat or seaplane. As soon as the tarmac had dried on the island's first runway, he landed there in the legendary DC-4, making his announcements in French and Tahitian, a language in which he was fluent.

Most of my early years were spent playing barefoot on the beach of *Pointe des Pêcheurs* in the area of the island known as *Punaauia*, with my best friend Paul, a blond-haired, blue-eyed half-Tahitian. We lived next door to Paul's grandfather, a prosperous coconut plantation owner, who became known to us as Papa Paul. My friendship with Paul has remained firm over the years, cemented as it was during those carefree, sun-filled days spent running in and out of the ocean.

It was with Paul that I first learned to surf. We didn't have any fancy boards back then but would simply throw large planks of wood into the sea and jump onto them. It took a lot of trial and error before we were able to stand up for more than a few seconds. However, once we did master the technique, we would spend hours in those waters, the colors of which ranged from the palest of turquoise through to the deepest of sapphire blues.

One of the few things to lure us back onto dry land would be the aromatic food that is typical of Tahiti. Even today, my mouth salivates when I conjure up the image of *fe'i*, large, orange-skinned bananas similar to plantains, and *uru*, breadfruit, both of which were cooked in baskets of woven banana leaves placed over hot rocks in a large hole in the ground, known as an *ahima'a*. (The word is derived from *ahi* meaning fire and *ma'a* meaning food.) The *uru* and *fe'i* were served as accompaniments to *poisson cru*, Tahiti's national dish, a South Pacific-style ceviche comprising the fish *mahi-mahi* marinated in lime juice, with onion, tomatoes and coconut milk. As diets go, it is a good example of making the most of what Mother Nature provides. It is also one filled with anti-cancer properties, which I had no way of knowing would turn out to be so important to me later in life.

Having grown up in such an environment, I miss the ocean if I am away from it for too long. I suppose I could sum it up by saying that the ocean is my church, and surfing is my religion. With the wound from my surgery healed and my stitches removed, I was itching to get back into the water again. The last time I had been on a board was in Cape Town just before my kidney "exploded." I was still a little nervous about pitting myself against the unpredictable force of the waves, but I reckoned my body was ready. I'd been doing plenty of stretching exercises and intensive jogging to get back in shape. I didn't plan on taking any stupid risks. I had also been checking the surf charts for a few days leading up to my trip, and it looked like conditions would be good for easing myself gently back into the waves.

It was well into September, during an Indian summer, when I drove the eight hours from just outside Paris to Biarritz, a coastal town in the southwest of France. Biarritz is considered to be the cradle of surfing in France, and was made famous during the 1957 film adaptation of Hemingway's *The Sun Also Rises*. Today, it is often referred to as the California of Europe.

It was already mid-afternoon by the time I checked into my accommodation, but I couldn't wait to get into the swell. After quickly changing into my board shorts, I headed off for the *Plage des Cavaliers* with my mini Malibu board tucked under my arm. I chose the Malibu because it's a good board for most conditions. I love its design, which goes from fiery orange through to a golden yellow. It reminds me of the sunsets that we surfers love to sit and watch at the end of a rewarding afternoon of wave riding. But, more importantly, it was while surfing on this board in Manly, Australia, that I caught one of my biggest waves, with a swell of around four meters. I felt that my Malibu might bring me some luck on this occasion too.

My chosen beach was less crowded than the more famous *Cote des Basques*. Something of an insider tip, the *Plage des Cavaliers* boasts a broad expanse of sand and is one of my favorite spots in the area. With at least three more hours until sunset and a series of gentle, glassy waves, the conditions were perfect for my first session in months.

I wasn't the only surfer in the water that day, so slowly I paddled out away from the colorful clusters of revelers waiting to catch the next ride. Just the movement of gliding my arms through the water felt so liberating. My scar, very visible and angry looking, was a little tight and uncomfortable as my body stretched across the board. I think my worry about opening it up again was making it worse. I wasn't wearing a wetsuit, since the ocean was still at a pleasant 71°F after the scorching days of summer, said to be the hottest on record in Europe for some five hundred years. I also wanted to feel the saltwater directly on my skin and allow its beneficial healing properties to work their magic. Gradually the tightness eased and my muscle memory kicked in.

Although the heat of the day had abated, the sun remained quite high, and its reflection on the water created ripples of liquid gold all around me. The resplendent beauty of my surroundings brought a lump to my throat. I thought back to my darkest days in the hospital, when I didn't know if I would survive. And yet here I was. I felt truly blessed to be here ... to be alive.

Closing my eyes, my face upturned to feel the gentle warmth of the sun, I offered up a silent prayer to the universal energy surrounding me. Since my strange, post-op experience in the hospital, I have no doubt that there is a greater force out there and, at that moment, I sensed that it was protecting and guiding me in all that I did.

Hearing voices nearby, I opened my eyes to see that I'd been joined by a group of four guys. Judging by their accents, they were Kiwis, three of them seemed to be of Maori origin. I nodded in their general direction and was greeted with return nods and a friendly chorus of "Hey bro!" The guys were younger than I, probably in their mid-twenties, and perhaps doing a gap year in Europe. I found myself catching a few waves with them. I was relieved to see that I hadn't lost my touch. We spent a good couple of hours in the water, paddling and chatting companionably about surfing. It's so easy to lose track of time when you're out there, but I always want to wait for that ultimate magic wave upon which to ride back to the beach. And when she finally arrived, she didn't disappoint.

Although no words were spoken, it was as though we had made a pact to ride that last, beautiful wave as a band of brothers. We were at one with nature, as we felt the mighty energy of the ocean lifting us up and propelling us home. For a moment, it seemed we were suspended in time. We experienced a combined sense of euphoria, of peace, presence, and pure adrenalin. It was the perfect ride with which to finish the day.

Back on the beach, my whole being felt utterly drained. Every muscle in my body was screaming in protest. I had put everything I had into that session, and it was all I could do to drag my board out of the water. Flopping down with a thankful sigh of relief on the still-warm sand, I attempted to catch my breath and calm my manically pumping heart.

The sun was now sinking rapidly on the horizon, turning

the sky into a swirling palette of fiery red and orange with abstract splashes of purple. My fellow surfers paused to appreciate this spectacle of nature with me, and together we watched as the sun slowly merged with the horizon. It was then that one of the guys broke the silence.

"Hey bro', I hope it's not rude to ask ... but ... like ... what the hell happened to your back?"

I sat up and protectively stroked my fingers along the length of my scar. I could feel it tingling in response to my touch. I imagined it must look alarming, the saltwater making it appear even more livid.

"Ah yes ... ," I began, "... my brush with the Great White." I momentarily enjoyed their shocked expressions, but soon broke my composure, unable to keep a straight face. I then proceeded to tell the guys my story and how it had been my first surfing session after the operation. My surfing brothers, just a short while ago so full of bravado and laughter, became quiet and exchanged glances.

An atmosphere of reverence permeated the space, and one of the Maoris stood up and said something to his friends in his native tongue. They too stood up and formed a tight huddle in front of me. They all then turned to face me, their backs to the ocean, and rhythmically they began to chant. As they did so, they bent their knees and raised their arms slowly above their heads before slapping their palms down firmly and loudly against their thighs.

I quickly realized that what I was witnessing was the *haka*, a ceremonial dance with which I was highly familiar, both from watching it being performed by the All Blacks rugby team, and also from my own childhood in Tahiti. Traditionally the *haka* was performed by warriors before going off to war. They used it to proclaim their strength and prowess in order to intimidate the opposition. Nowadays it is also performed to acknowledge the importance of a special occasion. It is always undertaken with the utmost seriousness and pride. To be on the receiving end of a *haka* is an incredible honor. The fact that it was happening to me on a beach in France felt little short of miraculous.

As their chanting grew ever louder, the guys' faces became contorted and their eyes rolled back in their heads. The air around us seemed to be filled with a powerful force that was being called forth through these perfectly synchronized movements. I could feel this energy vibrating to the core of my very being. As I watched the dance, my eyes began to tear up. These strangers had sensed that I had come a long way. Their gesture came directly from the heart as an acknowledgment of my journey and to empower me for the road ahead. I was moved beyond words.

In all, the *haka* lasted less than a couple of minutes. But these were two of the most intense minutes of my entire life. Even though I was too choked to speak afterward, my appreciation was obvious. The guys smiled, gave me a bro hug and then sank back down onto the sand as the sunset displayed its full glory.

CHAPTER 8

The Good Life

IN SEPTEMBER 2006, my career reached a new high. I qualified to fly the Boeing 777, a long-distance jumbo jet with the capacity to transport some 470 passengers. It marked both a professional and personal turning point, since I saw it as a confirmation of my renewed good health. After nine years of captaining the Airbus A320 to destinations within Europe, I felt thrilled to be in command of such an impressive long-haul aircraft.

My very first flight as captain of the "triple seven" was to New York's John F. Kennedy International Airport. It was also my first trip to the Big Apple since my days as a co-pilot on the Boeing 747. As was usual practice during the flight, I was given a separate meal, completely different from the rest of the crew. This is done as a safety measure to minimize the risk of food poisoning. Despite the strictest hygiene, statistics anticipate that one member of the crew will fall victim to food poisoning every month. This can have serious consequences if you happen to be flying the plane. As a result, the captain eats a different meal than that of his or her co-pilots. Not only is it different in content, it is also prepared in a separate kitchen to cut the risk of contamination.

After my brush with cancer, I had continued to be careful with my diet and avoided anything that clearly contained sugar. It pained me to turn down the tantalizing éclair au *chocolat* or strawberry tart that would often grace my carefully prepared captain's tray. However, I knew why I was making such sacrifices. I had fought hard to get back to good health and wasn't about to jeopardize it.

Elated, I landed the plane at JFK Airport a few hours later. Trundling through the rush-hour traffic, I already found myself looking forward to the familiar Novotel hotel in Times Square where the crew always stayed. After everything that I'd been through, it felt great to be back!

The next morning, I woke up early with the usual jet lag and was one of the first in line at the breakfast buffet. I was feeling hungry after eating just a light meal during the flight. There, laid out before me, was an incredible display of donuts. Knowing donuts were on my list of forbidden foods, I hesitated for a second as I again tried to listen to my inner voice of reason.

Memories rushed into my mind of Sunday mornings during my high school years, which I was fortunate to spend in Ohio. One of my favorite things was to go fishing with my pals on the nearby lakes of Indiana. It became part of our ritual to make an early morning stop at the donut shop and then head off with a carton of milk and a bag of those delicious golden rings. Good times!

Ah! I thought, *Why not? I've been so careful, and I've been cancer-free for nearly three years.* Feeling just a little guilty, I took the "contraband" back to my table next to the window, with its panoramic view of Times Square. The lights flickered on the billboards and reflected neon red, blue and green upon the glazing of the deep-fried doughballs on my plate. Licking a fine coating of sugar from my lips, I closed my eyes. *Oh, that taste!*

Indulging in two or three donuts from the hotel buffet returned to me a sense of normalcy. I was enjoying the same treats as everyone else around me. I wouldn't say that I had begun to take my health for granted but, as time passed, I did begin to feel as though I'd been given a Get Out of Jail Free card. I considered myself to be one of the lucky few. The every-six-month scans had now been replaced by annual ones, and the memory of my brush with cancer had started to recede. To my relief, every scan had come back negative and only served to reflect what I was feeling inside. I felt healthier than I had in years.

It was in this frame of mind that, upon returning from New York, I'd responded positively to a message from my brother. Perhaps worried that I was becoming a bit of a loner after my divorce, he'd suggested I meet the sister of a business associate.

The woman in question was called Heather, a Brit who worked as a freelance translator and had moved to Paris the previous year. Amused and somewhat surprised by my brother's blatant attempt at matchmaking, I decided to get in touch with this mystery lady. It seemed a bit like online dating, but with a lower element of risk since she had already been vetted.

When Heather replied to my email a few days later, I got the sense that she had been equally surprised to hear from me. We spoke briefly on the phone, and I asked her out for dinner. That's why, on one cold December evening, I found myself driving to Paris in torrential rain to pick her up for our date. Two years prior, I'd moved out of the miserable farm dwelling and bought a charming 150-year-old stone house in the quaint village of Apremont. The location was a short commute to Charles de Gaulle airport, but also remote enough to suit my need for peace and quiet. I usually avoided Paris, since I never feel comfortable in cities, but I was curious to meet Heather and decided to make the effort.

Despite having had a few casual relationships in the past couple of years, I felt unusually nervous on that evening. I worried that we wouldn't have enough to talk about. We knew so little about each other. I was also anxious that she would be high maintenance and turn her nose up at my choice of where to eat. In truth, I had scant knowledge of restaurants in Paris, fancy ones or otherwise. I also felt very uncomfortable eating in places that I didn't know, since I'm not someone who enjoys surprises. My one point of reference was the South African pub close to the Sorbonne.

In the end, my worries were unfounded. Apart from the incessant rain and the fact that I chose a rather dank and uninspiring Indian restaurant, in which we were the only customers, the evening was a lot of fun. (Turns out, my date had already traveled extensively throughout India and knew what real Indian food should taste like, which certainly wasn't anything like the food we ate that evening!)

Heather was different than other women I'd known before. She was something of a bohemian free spirit, having arrived in Paris after several years spent in Munich and then Vienna. She had wanted to change her life before turning forty and was lured by the romantic appeal of the City of Light. I came to learn that she was passionate about travel and had seen her fair share of the world, having spent many years backpacking solo throughout Southeast Asia for months at a time.

As the evening wore on, I found myself attracted to Heather on many levels. Not only was she striking to look at, with her long red hair and a scattering of freckles, but she also had a warm, engaging personality. She genuinely seemed like a nice person and was also a good listener. I spoke openly about my close call with cancer and my divorce. She took it all in stride, and the conversation flowed without any awkward pauses. By the end of the evening, I felt so comfortable with her that I suggested we round things off with a "Springbokkie" at *La Pomme d'Eve*, the South African pub to which I had sent the Under-19 team management to celebrate their win back in 2003. The celebration I had missed.

As we walked down the narrow stone stairs to the dark

cavern below, I felt a sense of anticipation. One of the TV screens was tuned in to a rugby match, while the Rolling Stones pulsated through the air from a speaker above the bar. I was back on familiar territory. It made me smile to watch Heather's bemused face as, in a ladylike manner, she sipped the potent mixture of the South African liqueur *Amarula* and French *crème de menthe*. This was definitely not the Paris that she knew! I gave her a reassuring wink, happy to be able to give her a glimpse of my world. I secretly hoped she liked it.

•————————•

I must have done something right on that cold and damp December evening because, less than a year and a half later, Heather agreed to marry me! I can't say that everything went smoothly from the start. My initial proposal had been made over the telephone, following a weekend during which we had decided to go our separate ways. To be honest, I had gotten cold feet about committing to a serious relationship and was still feeling jaded after my divorce. However, as soon as Heather walked out of my life, I panicked and realized I didn't want to live without her.

Unsurprisingly, she refused to accept my mobile phone proposal, which she received while walking with a friend along the *Avenue des Champs-Élysées*. I knew I would have to up my game in the romantic stakes.

I repeated my proposal a few days later when I opened a very good bottle of red wine in front of a roaring log fire at my home in the French countryside. I even got down on one knee to show her how serious I was. To my relief, she said yes.

Despite it being another cold and wet evening, not unlike the one of our first date, I afterward insisted on us driving to the magnificent *Chateau de Montvillargenne*, former home of the Rothschild family and where I thought we might get married. Here I ordered champagne, which we drank amid the grandeur of sumptuous red velvet chairs and ornate, gold-framed mirrors, both of us excited at the prospect of our future lives together.

We ultimately decided to tie the knot in Las Vegas. While it may sound as if it were a romantic impulse, in truth, our choice to marry in Sin City had more to do with avoiding the red tape required when a French citizen marries a foreigner in France than it did with any sentimental notion. Rather than worry about how to obtain certified translations of birth certificates, I simply requested a flight to Los Angeles on my monthly schedule.

We set the date for April 7, 2008. It seemed symbolic. Spring that year marked the five-year anniversary of when I was first declared cancer-free.

We arrived in LA jet-lagged but too adrenalin-fueled to sleep. After just a couple of hours of rest at the hotel, we rented a car and drove through the dry and dusty desert of Nevada in the early hours of the morning. Joining us on our road trip were two good friends of mine, Cliff and Patrick, whom I had asked along to be my witnesses. South African Cliff is a pilot for Korean Air and was able to fly in for the occasion, while Patrick is French and was my co-pilot on our flight to Los Angeles.

Upon landing in LA, I'd run into a friend who was the head of Air France ground staff there. Unable to contain my excitement at our "secret mission," I quickly spilt the beans and told her what we were up to. I also provided the link to a website where she could watch the wedding as a livestream.

We could have taken an internal flight to Las Vegas, rather than drive some 270 miles to get there. However, it was Heather's wish to have the all-American experience, which, to her mind, meant stopping off to eat at Denny's en route. Naturally, I didn't want to disappoint. Having seen the American diner portrayed in reruns of the popular sitcom *Happy Days*, Heather wanted to have the experience of sitting in a booth, being served endless refills of coffee by a waitress in a pink uniform. Denny's did not disappoint. Heather was pleased.

A few hours later, we checked into our room at the Bellagio Hotel and found ourselves looking out onto the Eiffel Tower. It seemed that Paris would never be too far from our romantic story.

We'd booked our slot in The Little Chapel of the Flowers for late afternoon. Bleary-eyed, we spent half an hour in line to purchase the obligatory fifty-dollar wedding license and then had a brief siesta before the ceremony. A couple of hours later, we made our way through the casino of the Bellagio.

I had changed into an uncharacteristically elegant suit and Heather was wearing a floor-length gold Suzie Wong-style dress, daringly slit to the thigh. (She'd had it tailor-made for her on an impulse in Kathmandu, while trekking in Nepal.) We both felt like extras from the Steven Soderbergh film *Ocean's Eleven*.

In front of the Bellagio, a dazzling, white stretch limousine, complete with champagne, awaited to take us to the chapel. In addition to Patrick and Cliff, our wedding party also included Heather's friend Christiane, who flew in from Portland, Oregon, and was accompanied by her friend, Kim. The six of us were in good spirits and any nerves, felt by Heather or me, evaporated as we sat back and enjoyed the somewhat surreal experience.

After the ceremony, we were the subject of a few kitschy romantic photographs that featured a quaintly ornate bridge and a floral arch. The photographer's biggest challenge was positioning the camera to keep the 7-Eleven sign from the store next door out of the frame. We then headed back to our hotel for a meal overlooking the Fountains of Bellagio, a large, dancing water display, complete with synchronized music and alternating colored lights. It was an unorthodox start to married life, but indeed a memorable one.

Back in LA at breakfast two days later, we were approached repeatedly and congratulated by much of my crew, as well as the crews from a few other airlines. Turns out, my friend had shared the livestream in the crew room at the hotel, and there were many who witnessed our nuptials.

A couple of months later, back in France, we repeated our wedding vows in front of family and friends at the *Chateau de Montvillargenne*. This was the place we'd envisioned when we toasted our engagement several months prior. Performing our blessing that day was none other than my good friend, Mervin Green.

My friendship with Mervin had gone from strength to strength following our initial meeting during the 2003 rugby tournament, when I had undergone the operation for kidney cancer. Mervin, who was by this time general manager of South African youth rugby, also held a license to practice as a minister. Accompanied by his wife, he flew over from South Africa especially for the occasion.

The day was blessed with sunshine and laughter. This time, Heather chose to marry in red and had a stunning dress made for her in Paris. Indeed, our wedding dance was to Chris de Burgh's *Lady in Red*. The words were fitting in so many ways, and I felt at peace, happy, and grateful to have "this beauty by my side," and to have been given a second chance in so many areas of my life.

Our wedding was followed by a honeymoon in Tahiti, where I retraced my childhood steps and took pleasure in showing my new wife the places that had been so important to me growing up, helping to create the person that I am today. We swam in the blue lagoons, ate fresh seafood and were lulled to sleep by the sound of the waves. It was a great start to married life.

Nevertheless, after a few months of wedded bliss, a

troubling cloud appeared on the horizon. Heather was finding it increasingly difficult to adjust to life in the rural backwater of Apremont, some twenty-five miles outside Paris. She had been used to the buzz of city life and was feeling a growing sense of isolation when I was away on flights. Her job as a freelance translator meant that she worked from home and had little contact with the outside world. I began to worry about her, and our relationship started to suffer.

We decided to take some time out and to spend a few days in Biarritz. I hadn't been back since my encounter with the Kiwis, but I'd told Heather that I could imagine living there one day. In my mind, this was merely a dream, perhaps one that would be realized when I retired. I only hoped, by then, I would still be in good enough shape to surf!

Heather also fell quickly under the charm of the seaside resort. She's not a surfer, but she loves to be near the ocean and was seduced by the beauty and history of this elegant little town. While I was battling against the might of the thundering waves, she happily meandered through the pretty streets and whiled away the time in beach cafes.

Halfway into the holiday, I woke up with a familiar, uncomfortable twinge in my back. I knew right away it was an old surfing injury that returns to haunt me from time to time, a sign that I've overdone things in the sea the day before. Reluctantly I accepted that I'd finished my surfing for this trip. And so, with just a couple of vacation days left, I accompanied Heather on a leisurely stroll through Biarritz. Like many tourists in a holiday mood, we decided to take a look at what the local real estate agents had to offer. I had no inkling that I was ready to move away from Apremont and its convenient proximity to my kids just yet, but I reckoned there was no harm in browsing.

It was in this frame of mind that we spotted a quirky little property situated within ten minutes' walk from the beach. Painted in blue and orange, the modest house exuded a holiday vibe. It was also a little lower in price than most of the others in the agent's window. I decided we should go and have a look. It might be a fun way to pass an hour or two. Having assumed we were voyeuristic time-wasters, the agent had left us to look around the property on our own.

Maybe I'd had too much sun and momentarily lost all sense of reality, or maybe it was the sheer pleasure at seeing the happiness radiating across my wife's face. Whatever it was, while walking through the property, something clicked into place and, as we were leaving, I turned to Heather and said, "Shall we change our lives?" Heather looked back at me, stunned, unable to believe her ears.

"Are you serious?" she finally responded, her eyes wide in amazement.

"Never more so," I replied, although I was beginning to wonder what on earth I was doing. "Come on. Let's go and see the agent before he closes the office for the day," I urged.

I wish I had taken a photograph of the agent's face when we walked back into his office that very same afternoon, and I put in a realistic offer. The deal was completed within three weeks. I'm sure it was the easiest commission he'd ever made!

I initially felt a little uneasy about moving farther away from my children while they were still in school, but I also believed that it was the best decision if I was to save my marriage. I was proved right. From day one, Heather was delighted at our change of circumstances. And although I had a tiring commute to get to work, life at home was blissful.

Before long we had settled into the coastal town and become acquainted with the stallholders at the market where we regularly shopped for fresh, organic produce. My rugby connections made our acceptance among the locals much easier, since the Basques are passionate supporters of the game.

September 2010 turned out to be the perfect Indian summer, giving me plenty of opportunities to hit the waves. Yes, life was good and getting better all the time. I truly felt that the dark days were behind us, and I looked toward the future with renewed optimism. I had a happy wife and a happy life. What could possibly go wrong?

A happy childhood spent in Tahiti
(a young JJ on the far left).

Around age fifteen, in the
cockpit of a DC-8.

An early passion for flying,
around age eleven in the
cockpit of my dad's
plane, a DC-8.

I had the privilege of being my dad's
co-pilot on the final leg of his
retirement flight from LA to Paris.

My father as a young
pilot in the US Air Force.

My father with his familiar pipe,
in the cockpit of a DC-10.

My mother as a young woman.

With Kelly, around age ten.

A young Jeff and Kelly.

With Jeff and Kelly
as young adults.

The venue for my wedding with
Heather: Las Vegas, April 7, 2008.

Taking our vows.

The wedding party!

A symbolic ceremony in front of
family and friends, conducted by
Mervin Green: Chantilly,
France, June 14, 2008.

Mum and Dad at our
ceremony in France.

Beautiful Biarritz.

In the hospital with my
"co-pilot" at my side, following
my initial thoracotomy:
August 2014.

La Grande Plage, Biarritz.

My first flight back to Cape
Town, South Africa, after
regaining my license:
March 10, 2016.

A warm welcome from the staff of
Crystal Towers Hotel,
Cape Town.

Proudly wearing my father's US
Air Force ring.

Jeff, a Springboks supporter
from an early age.

Preparing the changing room ahead of the Springboks game against France:
Paris, November 2017.

Outside the tunnel ahead of the game, with JJ Frederiks, the Springboks' operations manager.

With Springboks legends, prop Tendai Mtawarira ("The Beast") and captain Siya Kolisi.

Rethinking Cancer 2017, Institut Gustave Roussy, Paris, France, with Professor Alexander Eggermont (center) and Dr. William Li (right).

Rethinking Cancer 2017, with Dr. Bernard Escudier (left) and Dr. William Li (center).

Rethinking Cancer 2017, with Professor Valter Longo.

Rethinking Cancer 2017, with Dr. William Li and Professor Laurence Zitvogel.

Rethinking Cancer 2017, with Professor Thomas Seyfried.

Back on the left seat!

In the cockpit of my final plane, the mighty Airbus A380.

JJ with JJ!

CHAPTER 9

Relapse

BY THE SUMMER OF 2012, every day felt like it was a vacation. I was living the dream. I had bought a Vespa that Heather and I rode down to the local market, stopping for a coffee at our favorite beachside cafe. Here, we would sit and watch the waves and an eclectic parade of tourists walking by. On my off days from work, I joined the other surfers competing to catch a ride on the magnificent barrels of the *Cote des Basques*. Not that it all had been plain sailing. At times, the relocation had seemed like both the best and worst decision I'd ever made. The day we made the offer, I had become so carried away at seeing how happy Heather was about the possibility of starting a new life in Biarritz, I hadn't stopped to ask myself one fundamental question: *What if I can't sell our house in the north of France?* My failure to consider this possibility resulted in one and a half years of extreme financial worry and a great many sleepless nights. At my lowest point, I even toyed with the idea of moving us back to our old house and selling our home in this much-longed-for paradise.

Not wanting to burst my wife's bubble of bliss, I kept my darkest thoughts to myself. However, I often found it difficult to relax and appreciate the very things that our change in lifestyle offered us. While Heather would greet each day with gratitude, I began only to see the negatives of our situation—including the tedious commute to work, since I now had to take a plane to Paris followed by a one-hour bus journey between airports. Only then could I change into my captain's uniform and start the three-hour preparation for my own flight.

Salvation finally came when a long-awaited buyer appeared in the spring of 2012. I accepted a heavily discounted sum for our former home, but the relief I felt was priceless. At last, I was ready to enjoy life again.

Once relieved of that financial burden, I became fully immersed in our pleasurable routine, finding it harder and harder to leave for my "office in the sky." Fortunately, some long-haul destinations still held an irresistible allure. Among these was Reunion Island, a tropical haven of blue lagoons and stunning beaches set in the middle of the Indian Ocean.

In June 2012, I was elated to find Reunion Island on my roster. For several weeks I'd looked forward to this particular flight, especially since my previous destinations had been the bustling, smog-filled cities of Los Angeles and Tokyo. Our airline hotel was located directly on one of the island's most idyllic beaches, and I was excited at the prospect of plunging into the Indian Ocean.

Although it's a tough eleven-hour flight to Reunion, the workload is shared among a three-man crew — with two in the cockpit at all times, while the third member takes a two-hour break. My turn to rest came some six hours in.

I dozed fitfully during my allotted time, but it was only after returning to the cockpit that I felt some twinges in my lower back. The pain was akin to a series of intermittent electrical shocks. I figured I must have slept awkwardly in the bunk, but I began to feel increasingly uncomfortable. Nevertheless, adrenalin took over as we approached our destination, and I directed my full attention to landing the plane smoothly.

As I began to relax on the bus transfer to the crew hotel, the twinges reappeared and became more intense. Upon arriving, I went for a quick breakfast and then headed directly to my room. I felt sure that all I needed was a few quality hours of restorative sleep.

I awoke later that afternoon. The soreness had come back more intense than before. It seemed to be located behind the scar where my kidney used to be. Feeling concerned, I ditched my plans of going to the beach and instead set off in a taxi for an appointment with a local chiropractor.

Although, during the session, each manipulation felt like burning wax being poured slowly over my muscles, the visit seemed to do the trick. Afterward I experienced a sensation of lightness. I wasn't entirely pain-free, but at least I could walk upright without grimacing.

The rest of my time was spent relaxing on the beach. It was tough to lie in front of that glittering expanse of blue and not dive in, but I didn't want to risk triggering the pain again. Meanwhile, my mind shifted into overdrive. *It's impossible,* I thought. *Every scan since 2003 has come back clear.*

And yet the doubt lingered.

Back in my hotel room, I called my radiologist, Francois Paziot, MD, who had long since become a friend. Francois reassured me, telling me I most certainly had nothing to worry about after so long. Yet, to ease my mind, he agreed to do some scans upon my return.

Less than twenty-four hours later, the sand barely dusted from between my toes, I was back in Francois' office in Chantilly. Back in the same office where I'd gotten my initial kidney cancer diagnosis some nine years previously.

"I can't see anything," Francois muttered.

Relieved, I sank back onto his comfortable leather sofa while he continued to inspect the scans.

Thank God for that! I began to close my eyes. As I felt the stress leave my body, tiredness took over, and I started to relax. But just before my eyes shut completely, I saw my radiologist staring with greater intensity at the scan results on his computer screen. He was looking around the regions of the liver, the prostate and toward the lungs. And then he began to zoom in on one specific area, scrutinizing the same image from different angles. His expression changed.

"Well, I don't know …," he muttered, still staring at the screen. "Hmm ... very strange ..." He turned his attention back to me. "Actually, there is something here, JJ," he said, his voice now soft with concern.

He went back to the image and started comparing it to my last scan of almost one year ago. His facial muscles tightened.

"Yes, it appears there's something that wasn't here before."

I looked at him agape, unable to absorb what I was being told.

"I'm sorry, JJ ..." his voice trailed off as he reached for the phone on his desk. "I'd like to get a second opinion."

A few minutes later Francois was joined by Dr. Pierre Magdeleinat, one of the leading thoracic surgeons in France, who happened to work at the clinic with him. I remained in the room and anxiously watched the two experts confer quietly as they pored over the scan. Dr. Magdeleinat then looked in my direction, nodding in a matter-of-fact way.

"There's no doubt about it," he said. "You have metastatic growth in the right lung, probably originating from your original kidney cancer."

He went on to explain that the pain I had felt in Reunion was not directly linked to the cancer reappearing. It had probably been caused by my intestine moving over and taking the space that had previously been occupied by my left kidney. The intestine had subsequently become twisted and was blocking the normal passage of food. Had I not experienced the pain, then the cancer would have gone undetected for much longer. A lucky twist of fate, perhaps?

I momentarily caught my breath, unable to believe what was happening. I then switched back into my pragmatic pilot mindset, not allowing my emotions to get the better of me. Pilots are trained to follow a decision-making procedure known as the FORDEC. It's an acronym of the words: Facts, Options, Risks, Decision, Execution and Check. We are taught to apply this methodology to any procedure, checklist or situation that requires a decision. I instinctively knew that I had to apply the FORDEC to my own health. A problem had arisen that I needed to deal with. And fast.

Dr. Magdeleinat told me that I could undergo surgery but recommended I first meet with Dr. Bernard Escudier, a world-renowned expert on renal cancer. Dr. Escudier was based at Institut Gustave Roussy, Europe's leading cancer center, on the outskirts of Paris.

Not wanting to waste time, I urged Dr. Magdeleinat to make the necessary phone calls. Just a few days later, I sat in Dr. Bernard Escudier's office. He confirmed that his team had found four tumors in my right lung, and that these were growing. Dr. Escudier went on to explain a number of modes of treatment—surgery, immunotherapy, or a new drug known as an angiogenesis inhibitor, which starves tumors by cutting off the flow of blood supply that carries oxygen and nutrients Although the drug sounded promising, the long-term side effects were not yet known.

In line with the FORDEC approach, I looked at the facts and considered my options and the subsequent risks. I then shared with the doctor my concern that, as a pilot, any ongoing drug treatment would curtail my career. "I'm barely over fifty," I said. "I've got a few years to go. I don't want to stop flying like this."

My decision was taken. Dr. Escudier agreed to execute the surgical route and a date was set for a couple of weeks later. The procedure, which is called a thoracoscopy, would be carried out by entering my right lung under the arm. The keyhole surgery would involve three small incisions: one for the camera, one for the surgical tools and one for fluid evacuation. The final part of the FORDEC process, the check, would then come into play as my condition was monitored in the months following the operation.

I called Heather, but I didn't let on about my bad news. I wanted to tell her in person.

Back in Biarritz, I heard soft jazz music playing from the kitchen when I entered our home. Heather was absorbed in a recipe book.

"Hi," I said in a low voice, so as not to startle her.

She turned and looked at me, smiling. I stepped toward her and, as I did so, her expression changed.

"It's back isn't it?" she said, her voice shaking.

I nodded, unable to utter the words with which I was still trying to come to terms.

"How come? Since when?" Her questions hung in the air. I had no answers to give.

All that came up for me were more questions: *Had the*

tumors been missed on previous scans, perhaps too small to detect? Had the financial stress from the drawn-out house sale taken its toll on my health?

It was impossible to say. What mattered now was how we were going to deal with it.

When Heather and I first met six years prior, I had been very open about my unpleasant brush with cancer. However, with each year that passed, we had both relaxed into our new lifestyle and even begun to take my renewed good health for granted. I don't think either of us ever imagined the cancer could reappear after so many years.

Heather turned away, dabbed her eyes with a nearby tea towel and composed herself. Turning to face me once more, she managed a smile and put her arms around me.

"We'll get through this," she said. "You've beaten it before, you'll beat it again."

With that, she poured a large glass of wine for each of us. We would discuss the details of what lay ahead when I felt ready but, for the moment, we were going to enjoy our meal and a good drop of red.

Over the next few days we busied ourselves with preparations for my forthcoming hospital stay. I filled out the necessary paperwork and organized our flights to Paris. Heather took care of my sartorial needs.

"Honey ..." she called to me one morning from behind her computer.

"Yeah?"

"Green or red? Striped or checked?"

I looked at her blankly. The task of choosing a pair of pajamas appeared to have overwhelmed me.

She laughed. "Don't worry. I'll get them both!"

We arrived in Paris the day before the operation and went to a charming Parisian bistro for a "last supper." I indeed felt as though I were a prisoner awaiting the hour of my execution. The operation would be performed in a hospital named *Hotel Dieu*, which translates to hostel of God, and was located just opposite Notre Dame Cathedral. Neither the name nor the location gave me much comfort.

Perhaps I would be meeting my maker sooner than planned?

Appreciated from an architectural point of view, Hotel Dieu is impressive to behold. Founded in 651 A.D. by Saint Landry, a former bishop of Paris, it is the oldest hospital in the city. Built as a symbol of charity and hospitality, it was the only hospital in Paris until the Renaissance. Although ravaged by several fires over the centuries, its present architecture dates back to 1877. While I appreciated the Gothic magnificence of the hospital's exterior, I secretly hoped that the operating equipment would be more high-tech!

Heather spent the rest of the day with me but left in the evening so she could get some rest. I would need her to be in good shape over the coming days and weeks.

Once she'd gone, I had time to think about what lay ahead. I couldn't believe that I was in this situation again. I felt old and vulnerable. Within the space of barely three weeks, I had gone from being the confident captain of a Boeing 777 to again being a cancer patient, my gold stripes replaced by a humble nametag around my wrist.

I was grateful to have been given a private room, even if it was as austere as a monk's cell. The bare, yellowing walls, overhead strip light and lack of a window didn't do much to alter this impression.

A healthy right lung has three lobes. A fact of which I only became aware when my surgeon told me he'd removed my middle one entirely. The five-hour operation was deemed a success, and my two remaining lobes had been stapled together without any complications.

Heather and my daughter, Kelly, were sitting at either side of my bed when I awoke. I looked and felt like a zombie, but I was grateful to be alive and that my doctors had caught the cancer before it had spread any further. Now I had to concentrate on my recovery and rebuilding my body from within.

I once again saw that the food the hospital provided would not be much help, as it hadn't changed at all since my first encounter with it back in 2003. Again, the nurses tried to coax me to eat, treating me like a child, saying that I needed to regain my strength while presenting me with an array of sugar-laden desserts and entrees heavily processed to the point where they contained little to no nutrients. I refused their offerings and relied instead upon Heather to bring me vitamin-packed salads and fresh fruits, especially papaya. I had learned about the health benefits of papaya from Tahitian elders, who had recommended it for a large number of ailments. Possessing powerful anti-inflammatory and antioxidant properties, I felt it would do me good.

On one of her daily visits, Heather made the acquaintance of a young English-speaking couple. The woman, whose name was Helen, had overheard us chatting. It turned out that Helen was Irish. She was keen to share her story with a fellow Anglophone, especially since her French was limited, and stopped Heather for a chat outside my room.

"We recently got married," she said, gesturing in the direction of her husband, a young Canadian by the name of Mark who was sleeping in a room further down the corridor. As she told her story, her eyes began to fill with tears.

"Mark and I are here in Paris on our honeymoon. We were up the Eiffel Tower admiring the romantic view," she said. "It was then that his lung collapsed."

Heather later relayed the rest of the story to me. She told me that Mark had undergone a thoracoscopy the previous year. As a result of the collapse, the entire lung had now been removed. He was only thirty years old. The couple already had amassed a fortune in hotel bills while they awaited Mark's release from the hospital. Even then, their ordeal would be far from over, since they faced an arduous train and ferry journey back to their home in Ireland.

Upon hearing their story, I realized a detail that I'd not

yet considered. That I, too, would be unable to fly home on account of the pressure that would be exerted on my own lung. Heather sprang into action to buy first-class train tickets back to Biarritz. The journey time between the two cities is five hours, so we wanted to ensure that we would be as comfortable as possible.

Two days later when I was released from the hospital, French rail workers were on strike over a bid for higher pay. One out of every two trains was canceled, including our train to Biarritz. Our expensive first-class tickets now only gave us access to the train, but we had no guarantee of reserved seating.

At Montparnasse station, the platform was thick with people all trying to claim a seat on overbooked carriages. The scene reminded me more of Delhi in rush hour than anything I'd ever seen in France.

I shuffled down the platform. Each step sending shockwaves of pain through my body. I held a pillow against my upper body as a buffer against the pain and anyone in the fray who might knock into me, but it helped only a little. Heather carried both our suitcases, as well as a couple of smaller bags that contained my medical paraphernalia, all the while letting me lean on her as we walked.

Our portion of the train, which was continuing as far as Biarritz, was right at the end of the platform. With no guarantee of a seat, I dreaded the next five hours. At, least I had taken a heavy dose of painkillers, which helped to dull the raging soreness that was once more heating up in my lung.

My fears were confirmed upon boarding our hopelessly

overcrowded compartment. Nevertheless, we did manage to find the only vacant seat available. With enormous relief, I eased my way carefully into it before resting my head in exhaustion against the grubby window. Heather, meanwhile, stood in the packed corridor as the train jerked into action a few minutes later. We were only about half an hour into our journey when I became aware of voices around me. A smartly suited gentleman was pointing at my seat and brandishing his ticket with an air of entitlement.

This was too much for my normally calm and serene wife. Heather became agitated and began to speak animatedly with the passenger.

"Please," she urged, her face blanched with exhaustion. "My husband has just undergone a lung operation for cancer. He is in terrible pain."

Almost as bad as the pain was the sound of my wife pleading for me to have the seat. I felt a sense of shame seeping through me, but I also knew that I would have been unable to move. Even sitting down, I was in agony with every jolt. So, I kept my eyes closed and my head down. The tone of the conversation changed, and I surmised that I could stay where I was. As always, the mention of the *C word* seemed to do the trick. I was left alone.

"*Bon courage,*" the passenger responded in a gentler tone, wishing us both luck as he made his way back down the packed corridor.

Heather continued the journey perched precariously on our suitcases, stifling her sobs with a crumpled tissue. Her face was pale and her makeup smudged around reddened eyes. She had been brave for so long, but the stress had now caught up to her. I fervently hoped that the train would empty soon. However, it would be another two hours until we reached Bordeaux and a seat was vacated.

As the train rattled onward for the last stretch of our journey, I gazed listlessly out of the window at the endless rows of houses flashing past my eyes. So many different destinies: of sickness and health, of joy and despair. The speed at which we were traveling made me realize just how fleeting life is ... ultimately, we are all just passing through to our final destination. None of us knows what awaits us when we get there. What matters is that we make the most of each moment. Despite the weakness in my body, I was determined that I would get fit again. I would not give in to cancer. My own journey was far from over.

CHAPTER 10

Outside the Envelope

AS A PILOT, I have to stay focused all the time. The operating parameters and capabilities of a specific model or type of aircraft are outlined in a so-called flight envelope, which is a set of instructions written by the plane manufacturers. Any deviation, "flying outside the envelope," can put the plane and passengers in danger.

Even so, flying is not an exact science. It's like life itself. No matter who you are, one day you're going to face something unexpected. You're going to find yourself flying outside the envelope. That's when you find out what kind of a pilot you are. I decided to tackle my cancer with the attitude that I would use the experience to find out what kind of man I am. I wanted to be sure that no matter the outcome, I'd know that

I had done everything within my power to heal myself.

Once we got back to Biarritz, my recovery was hampered by a wall of fatigue unlike anything I had experienced before. I soon realized I'd taken for granted how easy it is to breathe, as every breath was now labored and painful, not to mention a cause for anxiety. Just thinking about the reconstructed lung area inside my body made me secretly worry about the repair coming apart if I inhaled too deeply.

To strengthen my lung, I undertook a breathing exercise comprising a once-simple act of blowing through a straw into a plastic container that was half-filled with water. Just a few minutes of blowing bubbles like a toddler playing with their milk left me so winded, any casual bystander would think that I had just tried to climb *La Rhune*, the tallest mountain in the Basque Pyrenees!

However, our bodies are resilient and responsive. The more we work them, the more they reward us for our effort. I found a physiotherapist nearby and, as soon as I was able to walk unaided for reasonable distances, I started to make daily trips to see him. Through a combination of deep, painful massage and equally taxing therapeutic movement, he helped me to regain my range of motion and strength, as I gritted my teeth at the hands of my "torturer." Heather met me after each session, and together we made the short journey up the small hill to our home, my arm clamped around her shoulder for support. While pre-surgery the walk took me only about ten minutes, I now shuffled and gasped my way home and arrived exhausted about thirty minutes later.

In contrast to the weakness in my body, my mind was sharper than ever. I began to spend my days scouring the internet to find scientific research on new ways to beat this illness. My methodology was simple. Since I do not have a medical background, I typed into Google basic inquiries, such as:

What are the new approaches to cancer?

How to kill cancer cells

Cancer and diet

The information readily available on the internet can be overwhelming and misleading, but my structured pilot mind enabled me to quickly determine what was most relevant to me. My research soon led me to a medical doctor and scientist named William Li and his findings on food and antiangiogenesis. Dr. Li had given a powerful TED Talk in 2010 entitled "Can we eat to starve cancer?" He also was the founder of the Angiogenesis Foundation, which is based in Boston.

While I had long been familiar with the toxicity of sugar as a substance known to nourish cancer cells, I wasn't aware of the process of angiogenesis, or that a wayward network of blood vessels is built up around each tumor, sending it life-giving fuel and oxygen. I read some more on the Foundation's website and learned that angiogenesis is the process by which our bodies grow new blood vessels and is a vital part of the process of wound healing as well as reproduction. The word "angio" (from the Greek word *Angêion*, meaning vessel or container) refers to the blood vessels, while "genesis" means creation. In healthy tissue, the body controls angiogenesis by maintaining a precise balance of growth and inhibitory factors. A disturbance in this balance results in either too much or too little angiogenesis. Abnormal blood vessel growth is observable in many diseases, including cancer.

The more I read about Dr. Li's approach, the more I became convinced I was learning something that had the potential to change my life forever. I was amazed to discover that many foods have been proven to combat cancer. The potential of this new awareness truly excited me. The Angiogenesis Foundation adopts research and methodologies that are traditionally used to test medicines and applies the same science to test various types and combinations of foods, beverages and ingredients. The purpose of this testing is to learn which foods are best at fighting disease, as well as to discover how a food's potency against disease is affected by cooking, processing and storage. Armed with this knowledge, patients can use foods as medicine to enhance the efficacy of drug therapy and, even more vital, to help prevent disease in the first place.

I instinctively knew that I had made a significant discovery for my own health. As is my habit, I wanted to share this knowledge with my loved ones. Heather and my children are used to receiving links from me to various websites about new approaches in health, breakthrough treatments or foods that we ought to be eating. I'm never sure whether or not they truly read them. My children tend to reply with a sigh of resignation and, "Yes, Dad ..." when I ask if they've received the info. I guess not everyone shares my passion for the world of science.

Heather was at the beach that afternoon. I called her in great excitement.

"I've just sent you a video. It's a TED Talk by Dr. William Li."

"Okay, honey. I'll take a look in a bit."

"You must listen to it now," I insisted. "It's really important." Adding, with my usual precision, "It will only take twenty-four minutes ... and twelve seconds."

"Yes, but I'm just relaxing here with a friend," she reasoned. "We're just out of the sea. I'll take a look when I'm home."

I wasn't entirely convinced by her response, but I went back to my research. The more I read, the more fascinated I became by Dr. Li's findings and his unique approach toward health.

On its website, the Angiogenesis Foundation states: "*Our vision is food will be the ultimate delivery vehicle for natural bioactive molecules that prevent diseases in their earliest stages.*"

Yes! I thought. *This is what everyone should be doing. Nature has given us the tools with which to fight cancer. It is up to us to learn how to apply them.*

When Heather arrived home a couple of hours later, I immediately brought up the subject of the TED Talk. She dismissed me with a raised eyebrow.

"I need to shower, and then I have a translation to finish. I'll take a look later."

I felt frustrated by her response, since I was eager for her to share my enthusiasm. My wife's eyes tend to glaze over whenever I bring up medical subjects. She leans more toward art and culture. When she turned on the radio and tuned in to a jazz station, I knew the discussion was over. For now.

That night before sleeping, Heather was propped up in bed already engrossed in a book. I turned to her and said, "I really want you to watch this video with me. It is going to change our lives."

My wife sighed and closed the chapter.

We proceeded to watch Dr. Li's TED Talk together several times, both of us fascinated to learn how certain foods and drinks can become more powerful when combined. Dr. Li gave the example of green tea, on which the Angiogenesis Foundation has done extensive research. Out of four commercially available varietals of green tea, Li and colleagues determined that Chinese jasmine and Japanese sencha were the most potent, and that a blend of the two was even more powerful than either alone.

"What we need to do now is systematically test and compare potencies between different products," Dr. Li said. "If you're selecting strawberries or wine, you want to know the most potent types."

"Well, that's good news," Heather grinned. "I love strawberries and wine!"

Even though, prior to my operation, I had returned to my low, low-sugar diet, after Dr. Li's talk and looking up several antiangiogenic foods, I realized that I could do much more to protect my health with food. I became determined to adapt my diet to include these foods that starve cancer by denying it a blood supply—foods such as tomatoes, tuna, green tea, lemons, grapefruit and, yes, red wine, to name just a few. I wanted to learn even more about angiogenesis, so I decided to get in touch with Dr. Li himself. I sent him an email telling him my story—no response. I called his Foundation and left a voicemail with his secretary. Still, I heard nothing. And yet I never considered giving up. Something told me that I needed to have contact with this man, that he would play an important role in my personal battle against cancer.

My persistence eventually paid off. After many attempts, I finally got through to Dr. Li's secretary, who told me that she would relay my message to him. Several days passed, and still I heard nothing. I called again. And again. And on the fourth time I struck lucky.

"Actually, Dr. Li is in the office now," his assistant said, perhaps realizing that I wouldn't stop bugging her. "Let me see if he's available."

A few seconds later, a kind and gentle voice came on the line.

"Doctor Li speaking."

I proceeded to explain my story, to which he listened with great interest, only interjecting to ask questions. At some point in the conversation, I mentioned the name of my oncologist.

"I remember Bernard Escudier!" Dr. Li exclaimed. "We actually worked together on early antiangiogenic treatment methods some fifteen years ago. Bernard was the principal investigator of the team. He's a very well-respected oncologist worldwide."

I was amazed. It seemed as though pieces of a jigsaw puzzle were slotting together—in this case, a jigsaw puzzle made up of brilliant minds, unafraid to turn conventional medicine on its head, and I was fortunate to be putting the puzzle in place.

Our conversation lasted forty-five minutes. Once I put the phone down, I decided to watch Dr. Li's TED Talk again. Toward the end, he made a comment I'd missed all the other times I had watched it, but this time, it struck me as crucial.

"Do we doctors do health care?" he said. "No, we do sick care in our modern medicine in the West. Health care should be what patients do for themselves every day."

I took those words to heart. I intended to do precisely that.

I have always been highly competitive and don't easily allow myself to be beaten. Nevertheless, I know that survival statistics for metastatic kidney cancer are not great, and I have struggled to keep a positive outlook at times.

After speaking with Dr. Li, for the first time since getting the news that the cancer had returned, I felt empowered. Armed with this new information, I would no longer have to wait for a costly treatment that would likely damage my immune system. Instead, I could take my health into my own hands and choose to eat only those foods that had been proven to have antiangiogenic properties.

Biarritz has a fantastic local food market called *Les Halles*, and I couldn't wait to go shopping. As soon as I was strong enough to ride my Vespa again, Heather and I headed off in search of powerful foods to combat cancer. The timing couldn't have been better. We were well into July, and the organic food stand overflowed with variety and was resplendent with the most vibrant of colors. The tomatoes really caught my eye. So red and luscious that they were just begging to be coated in a slick of polyphenol-rich olive oil, accompanied by a scattering of red onions, bursting with the antiangiogenic molecule quercetin, and roughly chopped parsley, with its powerful anti-inflammatory properties.

Tomatoes have gained a reputation for aiding the fight against prostate and breast cancer. It has been scientifically proven that the anticancer properties come from lycopene, which gives tomatoes their red pigment. In the case of tomatoes, it has also been found that levels of lycopene are increased through cooking. The use of olive oil, specifically, in the cooking process also increases the amount of lycopene absorbable to the body. Plus, tomatoes are equally rich in several other key nutrients such as potassium, vitamin A, vitamin C, calcium and iron. Even more exciting is the fact that the antiangiogenic potency is increased through the synergy of all of these ingredients as they interact with the lycopene. When lycopene alone and the tomato itself are tested head-to-head, the tomato wins every time. And they taste delicious too!

But, of course, tomatoes were just one of the weapons in my growing anticancer arsenal. Most vegetables are a good source of naturally occurring cancer-fighting chemicals. What is important to know is which ones are the most powerful and also how to prepare them to retain these health-boosting properties.

Heather threw herself wholeheartedly into the task of

providing tasty anticancer dishes, staying up late combing through Amazon, as an avalanche of cookbooks landed in our postbox. She also turned to Doctor Li's "Eat to Beat" website for guidance. Out went the previously much-loved whole-grain breads and pastas, and in came new ways of turning vegetables into flavorsome and appetizing dishes.

One evening, I walked into the kitchen to find her in the process of torturing a zucchini. I stared at a white plastic contraption into which the aforementioned vegetable was inserted.

"It's a spiralizer," she said in response to my puzzled expression. "We're having spaghetti tonight!"

"But you know I can't eat pasta," I protested.

My wife proceeded to turn a handle, which rotated the unfortunate zucchini toward a vicious-looking blade. What came out the other side were long strips of green "spaghetti." The result was delicious and quickly deceived our minds into believing we were eating the real thing.

I was relieved that Heather was so enthused with my new approach to eating and that she enjoyed trying out the new recipes, experimenting with an array of powerful spices, such as immune-boosting ginger and turmeric. I have always felt out of my depth in the kitchen and would have no doubt lived off tinned sardines and broccoli, if left to my own devices.

Not everything was a success. The cauliflower pizza crust sounded great on paper but, after two attempts ended up in the trash, we agreed to give that one a miss.

Cauliflower rice, on the other hand, turned out to be a good substitute for the real thing, but without the cancer-feeding sugars that white rice contains.

Heather embraced being able to take a more active role in my battle against cancer. For so long she had been my nurse, helping to bathe my wounds and physically support me when I was almost too weak to stand. Now she took great satisfaction in the knowledge that she was nourishing my body and her own at the same time. Everything that she put on our plates not only looked appetizing and tasty, but we knew how good it was for us as well. And, with each mouthful that I ingested, I imagined the molecules warding off any future tumors. My mind and body were becoming stronger by the day.

I was amazed and grateful to be back in the cockpit just five months after my operation. Every airline has a protocol to follow for pilots to come back, according to how long the sick leave has lasted. In my case, I had to go through three simulator sessions to show that I was up to the job. I am sure that my changed diet played a large part in my recovery. I became determined to stick to my new regime even when flying. I skipped the airline food and nourished myself on a mixture of raw almonds and pecans, accompanied by a glass of freshly squeezed lemon juice and hot water. While eating the same thing every flight might be monotonous to some, I knew how important it was to stay away from processed foods with empty calories. My strict dietary approach appeared to be paying off. I still had to undergo scans at six-month intervals but, with the first three coming back clear, I began to enjoy a renewed peace of mind. It was only when it came to scan number four that, once again, I got thrown out of the "envelope."

Heather always accompanied me to my scans, which I underwent at our local clinic in Biarritz. She usually sat at my side in the prep room, stroking my arm to soothe my nerves as the nurse inserted a needle for the contrast fluid. (As long as I can remember, I have had a fear of needles and have even been known to pass out.) Yet on this occasion, scan number four, I was so at ease that I suggested Heather stay in the waiting room. My wife happily agreed, since she was in the process of proofreading an urgent translation.

Prior to undergoing the scan, I spent a few moments discussing a shared passion for the ocean with my radiologist, Didier Vavasseur. We had become friends over the past couple of years, ever since my thoracoscopy. Didier loves to sail, and we chatted about his recent holiday. I felt relaxed and didn't have any pain to indicate that I might be in trouble again. However, when Didier called me into his consultation room shortly afterward, his mood had changed. I knew that something was up.

We took a look at the results together, and he pointed out what appeared to be clusters of nodules in both lungs. They were small, and he couldn't say for sure if they were tumors or just residue from my previous operation. A second opinion would be needed.

I returned to the waiting room to face my wife.

"All okay?" she said, barely looking up from the work she was proofreading.

"Let's talk outside," I replied in a hushed tone.

"Why? What's wrong, JJ?"

"Outside," I urged, indicating with my eyes that I didn't want to talk in the crowded waiting room.

Heather's reaction completely shocked me. She began to cry uncontrollably, tears streaming in a torrent down her face. Her hands clasped around her shaking body; she made a wailing sound that came from deep within. More like that of an injured animal than a human being, it was a cry of complete and utter anguish.

Aware of the eyes of everyone in the waiting room turned in our direction, I guided my stricken wife to the door. I felt overwhelmed both at the news I had just received and by the intensity of her reaction to it. Yet I tried to stay calm. The scan results were ambiguous and would need to be properly interpreted at *Institut Gustave Roussy*.

The timing couldn't have been worse. The following week I was due to fly my son to Singapore, where he would catch a connecting flight to Sydney. Jeff was now working as assistant manager in Little Jean, a fancy restaurant in the Double Bay area. I was so proud of the young man he had become, having transformed from a shy, hoodie-wearing adolescent into a mature and responsible adult. We had both been looking forward to this flight together, and there was no way I was going to let him down. Taking a fatalistic approach, I decided that I would only call my oncologist upon returning to Paris again. At least I would have had one special flight with Jeff, even if it might turn out to be my last.

CHAPTER 11

The End of the Road

BACK IN PARIS, my fatigue weighed on me like a heavy winter coat. The return flight had been punctuated with thoughts of my son, now so far away. I'd hated saying good-bye, unable to tell him my fears about the last scan. I hadn't wanted him to worry. And then, just before he'd boarded his plane for Sydney, Jeff had sent me a message. He texted that he'd gone back into the terminal before passing through the passport control. He'd hoped to give me a final hug, but I'd already left. Maybe he'd sensed that I'd needed emotional support too.

Once showered, I made my way to the Air France parking lot. In the comforting familiarity of my car, I sat in the dark and awaited the return call that would give me clarity. One way or another. Within a few minutes my phone sprang to life. For a split second, my hand hovered over the number now illuminated before my eyes. But I knew that I couldn't put it off any longer. Taking a deep breath, I pressed the green receiver icon. The familiar voice of Bernard Escudier came onto the line. Now on a first-name basis, Bernard and I share a personal and professional respect. Just as I am his patient, he has been my passenger on numerous occasions. This time, however, our conversation was brief. Bernard got right to the point, confirming what, in my heart, I already knew. The tumors were back.

I have always appreciated Bernard's no-nonsense approach. From the very outset I'd asked him to be straight with me, to not sugarcoat things. And yet this time his brutal frankness came as a shock. He told me there was no time to waste, that I would need to arrange an appointment to see him as soon as possible.

I hung up, rested my head on the steering wheel and closed my eyes in an effort to try not to panic. When the tears came, it was almost a relief, releasing the pent-up anxiety I'd been carrying the past couple of weeks since my last scan.

Wiping my eyes, I struggled to breathe normally. I knew that I must call Heather and tell her what was happening, but at the forefront of my mind were my children. I couldn't put them through this again, just when they were beginning to get on with their lives. The hard fact was we'd all been here before, but with so many scans coming back clean, I'd gotten lulled into a false sense of security.

I found myself thinking back to the awful day, eleven years earlier, when my kids came to see me in the hospital for the first time. It was immediately after that first operation to have my left kidney and, with it, a seven-centimeter tumor removed. I'll never forget the terrified looks on their faces. I had wept then too. Once they'd left, I had made a promise to myself that, whatever happened, I was not going to leave my children without a father. I wasn't going to die. One way or another, I was going to take my life into my own hands and find the answers that would lead me back to good health. I thought I'd done it. Now I wondered whether I'd gotten it wrong. Maybe there were no answers. Maybe this was it, and I had reached the end of the road.

⚫—————————⚫

A couple of days later, emotionally drained, Heather and I entered the oncology department of *Institut Gustave Roussy*. We walked in silence, having run out of reassuring words. I felt Heather's hand caressing my own as she stared stoically in front of her.

I had considered myself to be one of the fortunate ones. I thought I'd been "cured" twice so far. Had my luck finally run out? The answer lay beyond the closed door to Bernard's office, where I would find out if once more my doctor could throw me a lifeline, the faintest glimmer of hope. Or maybe he could not. There is still no cure for cancer.

Prior to my most recent scan, Heather and I had at last felt free from worry. I'd sold my house in the north of France. My children were getting on with the next stages in their lives. We loved our home in Biarritz. And I'd considered myself to be in great shape. Perhaps recklessly, we had thought we were untouchable, finally beyond the reach of the malicious disease that is cancer. And now our carefree existence was under threat once more.

We made our way to the waiting area, where the walls were adorned with colorful posters offering upbeat advice on coping with cancer, as well as promoting help groups for families, activities for patients, and fundraising events. It all sounded so optimistic. Almost fun. Like some kind of exclusive club.

Yet, looking around at the other cancer patients seated there, the stark reality was evident. Frail and drawn from relentless sessions of chemotherapy, some were bald with papery white skin, their red-rimmed eyes void of lashes. Men, women, children. Nobody was spared. The human body violently stripped bare, left exposed and vulnerable. This is a club that nobody wants to join.

Cancer is the cruelest of diseases. When it first struck me back in 2003, I'd felt robbed of my identity. Cancer had cast its dark and sinister shadow on my self-image. For a while, I had ceased to see myself as the successful airline captain I had been before. In the subsequent years, I had worked hard to regain my self-esteem, to look at my body without flinching at the scars which I wore like a collection of horrific tattoos. I couldn't believe that I was back in this position again, having to confront my innermost doubts and fears.

When our turn came, Bernard ushered us warmly into his office, and we greeted each other as the friends we had become. Once seated behind his desk, his tone grew serious. Clasping his hands in front of him, he looked me straight in the eyes before repeating what he had told me on our last phone call. The tumors were back and spreading throughout both lungs.

"Just how bad is it, Bernard?" I asked.

He looked across at Heather and me. Our hands were interlocked, a united show of strength. We both stared intently back at him, willing him to tell us that there is a miraculous cure. Something. Anything.

It was then that he dealt the hammer blow.

"Well, we do have stage four patients who are still doing well after three years."

Stage four? Three years? I tried to process the information that I had just received.

I am only fifty-four ... My children need me. My wife needs me. What about my job? This cannot be happening again. Not now.

For a moment I felt dizzy and thought that I might pass out, but I could sense Heather's grip tightening on my hand, bringing me back to the awful reality.

"What do you mean ... stage four?" I uttered.

"Your kidney cancer is categorized as stage four because it is highly metastatic. There are tumors in both lungs. The scan has also shown a nodule on the pleura. We need to act fast before it spreads further."

Of course, I had been in stage four when the initial

metastases were diagnosed in 2012. Maybe it was because they were small and few, but somehow the news hadn't really hit home back then. But this time, I felt the full force of Bernard's message. It was as though my mind had become some kind of bell jar in which my doctor's words ricocheted, pinging against the sides like a dozen flies desperately seeking an escape. I could see Bernard's mouth moving, but for a moment all I heard was the death knell. I had spent enough time on Google to know that stage four is the final stage in a cancer diagnosis. If you've got stage four, then you've been dealt the worst hand of all. You've run out of jokers. That's it. Game over.

Glancing at Heather, I was pained to see my shock mirrored on her face. I felt as though I had let her down. This wasn't what she had signed up for when we had married just six years prior.

Clearly accustomed to this pattern of conversation, Bernard continued, "I think we ought to consider the new treatment that we've been trialing. It's an antiangiogenic therapy, which is only offered to a certain number of patients. It has yet to be widely tested, but there have been some very positive results so far."

Bernard proceeded to take a cardboard packet out of a drawer and opened it up to reveal thirty pills, a one-month supply. The plain-looking drugs cost nearly $6,000 per packet, which is why they were not readily available to a large number of people.

I'm not sure why I was deemed a worthy candidate for

such an expensive treatment. I suppose I should have felt fortunate. I had become familiar with the power of antiangiogenesis through Dr. Li's work, and I was eating according to his guidelines. However, I also knew that angiogenic inhibitors had still to prove their efficacy in the long term. I felt that I would be a human guinea pig. I was equally aware that I was running out of options. It was then that I went into fight mode.

"No, I'm not ready for this," I said. "Not yet. Can't we operate again?"

I was determined to exhaust all avenues before being forced to give up flying.

Bernard sighed and told me that we would only be putting off the inevitable.

"Yes, the tumors can be cut out," he explained, "but they will come back and in greater numbers. At some point you're going to have to start a treatment. We would simply be buying time."

At that moment, buying time sounded good to me. Once I started a course of treatment, then I would most likely have to continue with it for life. I assumed that I would automatically lose my license. I doubted I'd be authorized to fly an airplane if I were taking powerful drugs that still were considered experimental. No insurance company would cover me—or indeed the airline—if anything went wrong. This is not how I had imagined ending my aviation career.

"I want to go for the operation," I insisted. "I want to give myself that chance. If the surgery doesn't work, then I'll start a treatment, but I need to feel that I've given it my best shot.

I'm not ready to hand in my wings just yet."

Bernard saw the determined look in my eyes and gave a nod of resignation. "Okay, JJ. It's your decision. I'll make some calls, and we'll get you in as soon as possible."

Leaving Bernard's office, I felt a renewed sense of purpose. At least I now knew what I was dealing with. The results of the scan had been another wake-up call. Over the past couple of years, I had once again relaxed my lifestyle in the assumption that I was cancer-free. Despite radically changing my diet to follow Dr. Li's antiangiogenic protocol, I had begun to indulge in the occasional slice of chocolate cake and maybe an extra glass of wine here and there. I knew I now needed to refocus on getting well and finding new ways to combat this disease.

The date was set for early August. I would require two operations, one on each lung, to be conducted three months apart. This time I would face a far more invasive type of surgery known as a thoracotomy. My surgeon, Dr. Magdeleinat, had explained that my lung would be accessed via an incision made in my back, between the ribs. The lung would then be deflated and brought outside the body, allowing the surgeon to physically feel for tumors and cut each one out accordingly. No matter how much surgery I had previously undergone, I couldn't help but feel anxious. It was then that I decided to take a more drastic approach to my health. I still had another card to play. It was one ace that I had been keeping in my chest pocket, but drastic times call for drastic measures.

It was time I stop eating.

CHAPTER 12

Life in the Fast Lane

WHEN I ANNOUNCED that I was going to attack my cancer cells through fasting and subsist purely on water, the reactions ranged from mild concern to incredulity and even shock.

"What do you mean ... but you're going to starve!"

"You can't! It's too dangerous!"

"You'll die if you don't eat!"

"How is it even possible?"

"It's total madness ..."

What many people don't realize is that the human body is well-equipped to cope with long periods without food, especially when it is given an adequate supply of water. Greek biographer and essayist Plutarch (AD 46–120) is even quoted as saying, "Instead of using medicine, rather fast a day."

Another more recent advocate of fasting to cure disease was American journalist Upton Sinclair. With fascination, I read and re-read his book *The Fasting Cure* (first published in 1912), in which he detailed his personal experience of fasting to improve his health. Also featured in the book were letters from readers who had cured their own illnesses, including cancer, after following his fasting advice.

The idea of starving cancer cells was something that I had come across during what by now had become my extensive research into cancer treatments. Although he did not refer to fasting specifically, German scientist Otto Warburg developed the hypothesis that cancer cells could not survive if starved of the glucose from which they generated oxygen. Specifically, Warburg had investigated the metabolism of tumors and the cancer cells. In 1931 he was awarded the Nobel Prize in Physiology for his "discovery of the nature and mode of action of the respiratory enzyme."

Once I'd believed I was clear of the disease, I had duly filed this information away at the back of my mind. Since the cancer had returned, I decided the moment had come to return to my mental archive, dig out my secret weapon and launch a surprise attack.

One name that had cropped up time and again in connection with contemporary fasting studies was that of Valter Longo, PhD, a professor of gerontology and biological science at the University of Southern California.

Prof. Longo, originally from Genoa, Italy, had arrived in California in his teens. The young Italian had dreamed of becoming a rock star, but it turned out that a traumatic event from his childhood had mapped out his course in life. At around the age of five, he had witnessed his grandfather die prematurely in his late sixties of an untreated hernia. As the young Italian matured, the allure of a musical career waned, and his interest in the sciences grew. In part triggered by the loss of his beloved grandfather, he became increasingly interested in the concept of aging. He decided to pursue science with the aim of understanding mortality and how to prolong life by preventing disease.

I first saw an interview with Prof. Longo in a captivating ARTE documentary made in 2012 entitled *Le jeûne, une nouvelle therapie?* (In English, *The Science of Fasting*), by the French husband and wife team, Thierry de Lestrade and Sylvie Gilman. The documentary focused on five places in which fasting is practiced on a regular basis: a Siberian sanatorium, a German traditional fasting clinic, a university clinic in Berlin, a colony of penguins in the Antarctic and, lastly, a university lab in Los Angeles.

In the documentary, I learned that, by the early 1970s, Dr. Yuri Nikolayev, director of the Moscow Institute of Psychiatry, had treated some eight thousand patients with fasts varying in duration from twenty-five to thirty days. The doctor reported that 70 percent of his patients exhibited a marked improvement in their condition. In 1973, skeptical of the Nikolayev's result, the Soviet Ministry of Health ordered two military doctors to conduct their own research into fasting. The researchers, Professor Alexey Kokosov and Professor

Valéry Maximov, confirmed the results and found that fasting provoked a mild state of stress, which in turn activated several recovery mechanisms or body detox known as sanogenesis.

Since 1995, the Goryaschinsk sanatorium on Lake Baikal in Siberia has used fasting to treat more than ten thousand patients for a variety of illnesses. Until the fall of the Soviet regime in the 1990s, fasting was covered by the public health system. Many of the sanatorium's guests now come from overseas.

The documentary also examined fasting strategies used at the traditional Buchinger Wilhelmi Clinic in South Germany, and it described approaches being tested in the United States by Prof. Longo and his team. After watching the film with Heather, I decided to try to contact Prof. Longo directly and tell him my story. I didn't hold out much hope that he would respond. He had gained a reputation as *the* reference in fasting research, and I assumed he would be swamped with inquiries.

I was astounded when, just two days later, he answered my email and suggested that we set up a Skype call. As had been the case previously with Dr. Li, speaking with Prof. Longo proved to be a turning point for me.

One of Prof. Longo's main areas of research concerned the beneficial effects of fasting for good health, especially in relation to its impact on cancer. He had conducted experiments on mice subjected to heavy doses of chemotherapy, and compared the ability to tolerate the chemo treatments of those that fasted with those that didn't. The early results revealed a drastic difference. Those that had fasted coped well with the chemotherapy, while those that continued to eat normally died.

Excited by his results, Prof. Longo had approached Dr. David Quinn, medical director at Norris Cancer Hospital, who agreed to work on a clinical study. In 2009, he published ten cases in which patients diagnosed with a variety of malignancies had voluntarily fasted on their own (for between 48–140 hours) prior to and/or (for between 5–56 hours) following chemotherapy. The patients each had received an average of four cycles of various chemotherapy drugs, in combination with their fasting. The results of the study suggested that fasting decreases the side effects of chemotherapy, such as headaches, nausea, vomiting and fatigue.

My first operation was scheduled to take place some two weeks after the Skype call. In order to best prepare myself for surgery, Prof. Longo suggested that I plunge into an immediate twelve-day fast. He stressed that it should be a water-only fast, if I felt up to it. He added that exercise would be essential, suggesting that I challenge myself by walking up hills whenever possible. He also recommended that I get a checkup from my doctor every few days during the fasting period. I felt excited and empowered to have something new to try. I hoped my tumors would, at the very least, be weakened once deprived of a food source.

Heather buoyed my efforts in this latest endeavor. Having previously lived in both Austria and Germany, where 15 to 20 percent of the population are said to have fasted at some point in their lives, she was familiar with the concept. In both countries, doctors often prescribe a *Fastenkur* to promote health.

Doctor Otto Buchinger, founder of three clinics that specialized in therapeutic fasting, wrote his book *Das Heilfasten* (*The Therapeutic Fasting Cure*) in 1935. He documented how he discovered the benefits of fasting in 1918, when he had been decommissioned from the German navy following an episode of acute rheumatic fever that rendered him an invalid. After undertaking a nineteen-day fast, he regained the mobility of his highly inflamed joints. Buchinger founded his first fasting clinics in the German towns of Witzenhausen and Bad Pyrmont. His book, as well as many articles and publications, inspired the opening of two more clinics, in Ueberligen (Germany) in 1953 and Marbella (Spain) in 1973. The doctor was awarded the Federal Cross of Merit for his pioneering work. Today his vision is continued by the fourth generation of his family, including four great-grandchildren, his grandson Raimund Wilhelmi and Raimund's wife, Dr. Francoise Wilhelmi de Toledo, now one of the most esteemed fasting experts worldwide and author of countless scientific publications on the topic.[2]

Though it's an area that has been getting more attention in recent years, fasting has been around since time immemorial. Over the multiple millennia of our evolution, people have had to adapt to seasonal climate changes when food became scarce. Prof. Longo explained how our bodies are dependent on fasting to survive but, owing to high-tech food conservation methods, we've become unaccustomed to it. Our modern way of life, with its excesses of consumption, has only made the lack of fasting phases more damaging to health now that so much of what we eat is ultra-processed and junk food. As a result, we are getting fatter and fatter on a global scale, and much of this has been caused by misinformation fed to us by health authorities.

The first US dietary guidelines, published in 1977 by the Select Committee on Nutrition and Human Needs, recommended a decrease in the consumption of fatty foods such as meat, milk and eggs. These recommendations were adopted by the US government and the American Heart Association (AHA), which began urging Americans to restrict the amount of fat and cholesterol in their diets. Consumers were urged to buy leaner meats and foods lower in saturated fats and cholesterol. The result was a whole new industry of low-fat, "diet" foods.

Many scientists knew that not all fat was bad, and some argued against the new measures, but their voices fell on the deaf ears of the politicians. As fat was removed, sugar was added in. One of the reasons for this was to regain some of the flavor that had been lost with the fat.

Between 1977 and 2000, Americans doubled their daily sugar intake, and sugar—as opposed to saturated fat and cholesterol—is the primary culprit causing weight gain. Eating good fat does not make you fat. Eating sugar does. It causes obesity, diabetes, cancer and a whole host of other diseases. I recently saw a photograph of tourists on a beach in 1970. Everyone, without exception, looked slim and fit.

Compare that image with one of today. The picture is very different indeed!

Even the famed good health and longevity of the Japanese in Okinawa, reputed to have the highest concentration of centenarians in the world, is under threat of losing that status due to a rapid increase in obesity caused by adopting Western lifestyles. One clear shift apparent in recent years is that *Oomori* (large size) has begun to appear as a menu option in Japanese restaurants.

The more I read through the research, the more convinced I became that fasting could be the answer to a whole spectrum of health problems, cancer included.

Here's how it works:

STAGE ONE (DAYS ONE TO TWO)

The body has two main fuels: glucose and fats. When a person is eating a typical diet of carbohydrate-rich foods, the body breaks down sugars and starches into glucose. After ten to fifteen hours of not eating any food, insulin levels drop followed by that of the blood glucose, which stabilizes at the lower end of the normal range. Liver glycogen (a stored form of glucose) is then converted into glucose and released into the blood. This reserve is only sufficient for half a day. It is then that the metabolic switch from glucose to fat and "ketone" bodies takes place. (Ketone bodies—or simply ketones—are chemicals made in the liver from fat to act as a glucose substitute, especially for the neurons.) The efficiency of this switch can be enhanced by two to three hours of exercise, which also favors the formation of ketones. Exercise and natural practices such as phytotherapy (light therapy), massage and yoga, among others, equally play a central role in stimulating the organs of elimination (liver, skin, kidney, intestines and lungs).

EARLY STAGE TWO (DAYS TWO TO THREE)

Hunger starts to diminish. The body is now using stored fat and ketones for energy, as well as a small percent of body proteins. This stage, referred to as ketosis (or the "protein sparing stage"), is the central mechanism of fasting. At this point the main work is being undertaken by the liver, which acts as a factory for transformation. One sign that the body is in ketosis is a characteristic smell on the breath. A heavily coated tongue can be a common symptom in this initial phase, resulting from changes in the microbiome.

The fasting process also produces a physiologic acidity in the blood, creating a state referred to as fully compensated metabolic acidosis. A general sense of fatigue may be experienced during one to three days, as well as nausea and headaches or lower back pain, but these effects are generally transitory. This period is characterized by increased autophagy, a natural cellular cleansing and recycling mechanism. Autophagy can also destroy old and damaged mitochondria (our cellular "power plants"), which will then be rebuilt stronger and with greater potency.

The sensation of hunger disappears in the first three days of fasting, as neurohormonal changes and ketosis take place.

LATE STAGE TWO (DAYS FOUR TO FORTY OR MORE, ACCORDING TO THE BASELINE WEIGHT)

Now the body cells feed mostly on fat; the remaining small percentage comes from proteins that are drawn from all organs, including the muscles. After four days of fasting (in the case of a long-term fast), many people report periods of increased energy, mental clarity and an enhanced mood.

A long-term fast can last anywhere from five to twenty-one days or more. Many have continued to fast for much longer periods without suffering any detriment to their health. Of course, it is important to have medical supervision during a fast to ensure that the body doesn't develop deficiencies or dysfunctions. Most importantly, drugs need to be adapted or suppressed by a physician. Furthermore, the fasting must absolutely be followed by a very progressive and disciplined period of food reintroduction. A ketogenic anti-angiogenic diet with time-restricted eating seems today the most appropriate nutrition for cancer patients after fasting.

The longest fast ever documented in a scientific publication dates back to 1965. It was undertaken by Angus Barbieri, a twenty-seven-year-old Scottish man. Morbidly overweight, Barbieri fasted for 392 days—initially under the guidance of researchers from the University of Dundee and then on his own. Weighing in at a staggering 472 pounds at the start of the fast, the patient was down to a healthy 178 pounds at the end of it. During this time, he went entirely without solid food, surviving purely on tea, coffee, water and vitamins. Angus Barbieri reportedly broke his fast with a breakfast of one boiled egg accompanied by some bread and butter. (Although this might not have been the ideal way to do it!)

Five years later his weight was still at a respectable 196 pounds. In 1971, his fast was recognized by Guinness World Records and, to this day, remains the longest documented fast of its kind. Naturally, I had no interest in breaking any records, but I was determined to capture the benefits of fasting for my own health.

MY PERSONAL FASTING EXPERIENCE

As anyone who has undertaken a fast will know, the first four days can be tough, especially when you suffer from a severe illness, as I did. I experienced hunger pangs along with an overwhelming sense of fatigue and lack of energy. I went walking every day with Heather around the lake near our home, attempting to climb a few gentle slopes, but it felt like she was dragging me.

Although my hunger finally disappeared on day four, I still felt lethargic and irritable. And then, on day five, something remarkable happened. I woke up feeling bright, alert and full of energy. Over the next few days, my walking pace picked up and, on day nine, I was zooming around the lake like a mad speed racer. By this stage, Heather could no longer keep up with my multiple laps and instead preferred to wait for me on a bench once she had completed a leisurely walk on her own.

The change was extraordinary. Denied glucose derived from food, my body cells had begun to feed themselves on my adipose tissue, which is the connective tissue consisting mainly of fat cells. Meanwhile the cancer, which needs sugar to survive, was being slowly starved. I finished the fast almost eighteen pounds lighter, and I felt euphoric.

In some ways, I found my fast easier to cope with than Heather did despite— or maybe on account of—the fact that she was still eating normally. Whenever it came to mealtimes, she would try to hide away from me, so as not to stimulate my appetite. This wasn't an easy task, since our kitchen and living area are all in one open floorplan. Consequently, there wasn't much she could do to prevent tantalizing food aromas from wafting under my nose.

"How was your dinner?" I said one evening, feigning casual disinterest.

"Okay, nothing special," Heather replied a little too quickly, as she attempted to push a plate of thirty-six-month-old Gouda, velvety red grapes and a half-finished glass of wine out of sight.

No doubt she intended to follow this with her favorite dark chocolate. At least I approved of her choices. They all were highly antiangiogenic! Watching television also proved to be a challenge. It's a little like going through a breakup, when all you hear on the radio are the tragic songs of love and loss. When you decide to stop eating, you can guarantee that all you'll see on the "gogglebox" are food commercials and cooking programs.

I also found I had a lot of spare time on my hands, since a normal day would otherwise be punctuated with mealtimes. And then there was the small issue of bad breath, testimony of my disturbed microbiome. A fact of which Heather frequently reminded me by doling out sugar-free mints at regular intervals. Despite the challenges, I never once felt like straying from my chosen path. My eyes were firmly fixed on the target.

Three days prior to my operation, I underwent a full upper-body scan. This is a routine procedure to ensure that the surgeon has the very latest information before going in. The results were far better than I ever could have imagined. Not only had there been no further tumor growth, but five of the ten tumors in my right lung had undergone necrosis. Put simply: they were dead and no longer a threat.

My surgeon, Dr. Magdeleinat, could not believe it. Sitting opposite me in his office, his hand stroking his chin, he again studied the files in front of him before looking at me intently.

"What did you do?" he asked, perhaps expecting to hear that I'd taken some revolutionary new drug.

"I stopped eating," I replied in a matter-of-fact tone.

"What do you mean? Nothing? Not even a snack?"

"Nothing. Just water." I proceeded to explain about the twelve-day fast, to which he listened with great interest, his eyes widening in disbelief.

Clearly unaccustomed to patients taking such action before an operation, my surgeon removed his glasses and rubbed his eyes. "I didn't know you could even live for that long without eating," he joked.

However, the results spoke for themselves. Half of the tumors were no more. I got a huge psychological boost from having been able to affect such a positive change on my body, and I approached the first operation with a renewed sense of positivity and optimism.

CHAPTER 13

Back in the Ring

FASTING HAD BEEN a positive experience for both my mind and body, but the fact remained I still had tumors in my lungs that, left unchecked, would grow and spread to other organs.

I've always appreciated the support I have received from everyone around me, but I'd come to a point where I knew that the fight was mine, and mine alone. I was the one with my back against the wall. And no matter how much my supporters wanted to help me win, all of them—my wife, my children, my parents and friends— were spectators, cheering me on from the stands. At times, I felt like a battle-weary gladiator being paraded out into the arena, waiting for the next bout to commence. And I was conscious it could be a fight to the death.

Waiting was the worst of it, since I didn't know when the next attack would come or how ferocious it would be. With these thoughts circulating in my mind, I was once more wheeled off to the operating theater.

Coming around from the six-hour operation on my right lung, I must have looked like Frankenstein's monster. A drainage tube had been inserted in my side via my ribs, an IV to deliver pain medication was inserted into my arm, an oxygen tube protruded from my nose and a catheter was attached to ... well, I wouldn't be leaving the bed for a while.

I used the pain relief pump frequently over the days that followed and, as a result, everything became pretty much a blur. All I knew was that the surgeon had removed all ten tumors, the dead ones as well as the active ones, and that I would be sent home to recover before having to go through it all again in a couple of months. Operation number four, this time on my left lung, was scheduled for November. Being tumor-free by Christmas would be the best gift I could hope for that year, although I knew by now from experience that the cancer was likely to return.

Back in Biarritz, Heather looked after me with her accustomed calm, and we paid the bills through the private aviation health insurance policy I had been paying into since I started my career. Dad had always encouraged me to be fiscally responsible, and I was thankful I'd listened to him, so we didn't have any money worries while I undertook the slow process of post-op recovery.

My dad had looked out for me at every point in my life. When I was a young boy, I'd left Tahiti to continue my education in France, but I didn't fit in at the local school. The contrasts between the two countries were extreme. In Tahiti, I had experienced nothing but kindness and smiles from my Tahitian teachers. Clad in their flamboyant floral shirts and with Tahitian gardenia or *tiaré* flowers tucked behind their ears, they taught against a backdrop of constant blue skies and brilliant sunshine, with the fragrance of coconut oil wafting through the windows. At the end of the school day, I would swim and surf with my Tahitian buddies. I didn't have a care in the world.

Back in France, everything appeared to be gray and cold, from the skies to the austere school buildings. Gone were the friendly smiles, replaced instead by piles of homework and punishment. I was treated as an outsider by my fellow students and teachers alike, who mocked me for my funny accent. (I had adopted the habit of rolling my Rs in the Tahitian style.) My discomfort meant that I also avoided direct eye contact, with the result that I was seen as rude and difficult. Shouted at and ridiculed by my teachers, and bullied by my classmates, I closed up emotionally and fell behind in my studies.

My father was the one who suggested I go to America to complete my education. He could see I was failing to thrive in France, and that the US, where I had spent many summers at camp, was more suited to my personality.

At St. John's High School in Toledo, Ohio, I finally found my feet. The school gave me every opportunity to be myself, to learn and try new things. The American system encouraged open communication between the students and teachers, who concentrated on my abilities rather than on the things I didn't do so well. Sport was a big part of American school life, with teamwork playing a key role. I took up cross-country running and soccer, making great friends in the process, some of whom I still stay in touch with to this day. As a result of this different approach to education, I also grew in confidence, and my grades shot up.

When I reached the age of nineteen, my dad said that he would pay for me to learn to fly. At the time I was torn because I had been given the chance to attend a university on account of my soccer skills. However, my father made me realize the opportunities that I would have through a career in aviation. Therefore, I completed a six-month intensive program in the US, which was followed by almost one year of work there, before I returned to France. Once back in Europe, I attended another flying school to convert my American license into the French one.

At the age of twenty-one, fresh out of flying school, I was desperate to secure work, but there were no jobs to be had in either America or France. Again, my dad stepped in and found me a job in Ivory Coast, West Africa.

It was a tremendous training ground, since the poor equipment and volatile weather meant that challenging situations arose out of nowhere. Flying in tiny single- and twin-engine planes I faced many hair-raising moments, ones where I could have been killed had I not been able to make split-second decisions without panicking.

As a young pilot with little practical experience, I was forced to trust my gut. I remember one particularly terrifying incident when transporting the personal architect of the then-president of France, François Mitterrand, to the capital of Ivory Coast, Yamoussoukro. We had to fly through horrendous storm conditions for over an hour, during which time the plane was tossed around like a paper kite. To make matters worse, water started to leak through the roof into the passenger area. Sensing movement behind me, I snapped my head around to see my VIP passenger shifting awkwardly as he tried to avoid getting wet. Using my eyes and a hand gesture, I indicated that he should move to a different seat. Little did he know that getting wet was the least of his worries.

Unable to see the tip of the plane's wing, and with no visual reference on the ground, my mind and body kept telling me that the plane was going into a steep dive. However, my instruments indicated that I was still flying straight. Planes of this type only had one set of instruments, so there was nothing else to fall back on.

What if the instruments have failed? screamed a voice in my head. Nevertheless, I had no choice but to trust the instruments. I landed the plane safely, but my nerves had taken a battering.

On another occasion I had to land the plane at night on a short bush runway made of red earth and with no lighting.

My only guidance in that impenetrable blackness was a car at the start of the runway with its headlights on full, pointing me in the right direction. To compound matters, the area was surrounded by mountainous terrain. I couldn't afford to make a single mistake. Just five minutes before my descent, the primary lighting system in the cockpit failed. I had to rely on emergency lighting, which was a little like driving a car in the dark when your passenger turns on the central overhead light to read a map. My eyes were blinded by the glare, and yet I still had to focus on what lay ahead. After two go-arounds, I managed to touch down safely, but it was a close call.

Sadly, a dear friend was not so lucky. He had been flying from Accra to Abidjan when a monster storm cut all the power to the city, leaving it plunged in total darkness. My friend was running out of fuel and had no more navigation aid or means of visibility. The next day his crashed plane and lifeless body were found at the first light of dawn. It was a sobering lesson for a young pilot like me. Through this tragedy, I learned that thinking quickly and keeping calm are the best tools in a pilot's armory. That, and luck. Yes, there's always an element of luck. I pray every day that I'm lucky in my fight against cancer.

In November 2014, I prepared for the second thoracotomy, this time on my left lung. It was another grueling six-hour operation and, as always, I awoke to see Heather and Kelly at my side. Kelly had grown into a young woman, and I felt proud of her and the courage that she had shown throughout my battles with cancer. Jeff was working in Sydney, so Kelly called him on Skype and placed the phone next to my ear. I vaguely remember speaking to my son before losing consciousness again. I knew that I was fortunate to be surrounded by so much love.

Just four days after the operation, I persuaded my doctors to let my friends take me out of the hospital to go to the *Pomme d'Eve*, the South African pub in Paris, so that I could watch the Springboks play the test match against Wales. The junior doctor on duty expressed strong objections. Upon making his rounds, he was shocked to see me struggling to change from my hospital pajamas into my regular clothes.

"Where do you think you are going, Mr. Trochon?" he said, his voice rising in surprise.

"The Springboks are playing!" I exclaimed, adding that they were a rugby team when I saw the blank expression on his face.

"You can't just leave. You're not strong enough."

"I've never missed a match," I replied. "I'm not going to start now."

Seeing the determination on my face, he agreed to call Dr. Magdeleinat to check if it was okay. My temporary release was approved on the condition that I return immediately after the game. I felt like a wayward teenager being placed under a curfew. However, being with my friends and watching the match gave me a much-needed sense of normality. The Boks were a part of my life; they were my other family.

I felt the eerie echoes of being in a similarly vulnerable state in 2003 when I had gone to watch the Baby Boks in the semi-final against France. I recalled how the team slogan, My Blood is Green, had been announced at the time of that first operation. I still relate to this today. I wear the green jersey with pride whenever I watch a Springboks game. In few other countries, do the nation's sports teams include so many colors and ethnicities. I strongly identify with this diversity on account of my own unconventional upbringing. I feel I am a composition of several different identities and cultures mixed together. I am one individual in a larger, diverse group but, at the same time, I am part of a unified team.

Supported by the arms of my wife and Gilles, a friend who worked in international relations for the French Rugby Federation, I managed to hobble the few meters down the corridor of my hospital ward and out to a waiting car that whisked me to the pub a mile away. Since Gilles had already phoned ahead, the bar's owner, George, and staff were waiting for me, with a special seat reserved in front of a giant TV screen.

Meanwhile, at the Millennium Stadium in Cardiff, I knew that the Springboks would be going through their strict pre-match protocol. Having been their liaison officer for the past fifteen years, I could picture them arriving in their team bus accompanied by a police escort. Previously, when they had played in Paris, it had been my job to lead them in silence from the bus to the changing room. Once inside, every minute is accounted for as the players mentally prepare for the match ahead.

I therefore couldn't believe it when the Springboks texted me a picture of themselves in the changing room at Cardiff while they waited to go onto the field. Looking at that photograph on my phone brought tears to my eyes. It was the last thing I expected. I knew how much pressure they would be under in those final few moments before heading out to pit themselves against the Welsh Dragons. The fact that they had broken protocol to take precious time out to send me a picture meant more to me than the game itself.

Witnessing my team play with my friends seated by my side, laughing and cheering, filled my heart with gratitude. Even though the Boks lost 12–6 to Wales, I felt like a winner. In that moment, I stopped identifying myself as a cancer sufferer who aroused feelings of pity; I again felt strong and in charge of my life. Illness can be horribly isolating. Watching the game at the pub was just what I needed to lift my spirits. When I returned to the hospital later that evening, tired but happy, all the nurses remarked on the mental switch that had taken place within me. I had gone from being anxious about my survival to gaining a sense of lightness and a renewed determination to live.

Yes, physical recovery is important, but the power of the mind is so much stronger than we give it credit for. I needed to feel part of a team again, to be connected to everything that I loved. It was a comfort to know that, underneath the angry wounds of my recent surgery ... my blood was still green.

CHAPTER 14

K for Keto

CHRISTMAS 2014

Several dozen succulent oysters glistened on the silver platter in the middle of my parents' dining table. Accompanying these briny delicacies were the plumpest of king-sized prawns. Sautéed to a flush of pink and moist with olive oil, they were nestled in pearly abalone shells, a cherished family heirloom from our years in Polynesia. Taking center stage, however, were two enormous lobsters, each displayed on a large, gold-rimmed porcelain plate that was slightly chipped and faded with age. To the side sat slices of lemon and dollops of delicious, garlicky aioli.

With the seafood devoured and greasy fingers wiped clean, it was then time for the *pièce de résistance* of our

Christmas feast: the *Bûche de Noël*, or yule log. Our preference was for a rolled sponge cake filled with ice cream, rather than the more traditional buttercream filling. In keeping with our tradition, Mum had ordered two types of ice cream bûche, one was a fruit version bursting with luscious berries and the other the darkest of chocolate. The chocolate one was my personal favorite, a fact that my mother knew all too well.

As is customary in France, my family celebrated Christmas on the eve of December 24. My mother loved it when we all came together, and she would preside over the meal preparations like a proud, if somewhat diminutive, lioness.

Only the finest silverware would do, and she also pulled out her vintage champagne *coupes*, as well as a selection of crystal glasses in a variety of shapes and sizes for serving an array of red, white and dessert wines. Over the years, my parents had become experts in the art of entertaining. It was a ritual that had begun in Tahiti with their sundowners of rum-based cocktails enjoyed among friends, as they watched many a fiery sunset slowly sink over the lagoon.

At Christmas celebrations in Tahiti and later in France, my dad would sit at the head of the table and smoke his pipe as he regaled us with stories of his years as a fighter pilot. We had heard them all before but I, for one, loved hearing them time and again. Laughter was never in short supply around our table.

My parents' family table had swollen with the addition of husbands, wives, children and grandchildren. My siblings and I would carry additional chairs from the basement storage area as we crammed together in my parents' apartment, raising our glasses to our good fortune and the festive feast. However, in recent times, our number had diminished. Other sets of grandparents and in-laws demanded the presence of their offspring. That year, Heather and I were the only family members to join my parents in Toulon.

Despite having only four at the dining table, Mum had ordered food for twelve, as she'd grown accustomed to doing. Now too handicapped to undertake the shopping herself, the days leading up to the main event were preceded by a flurry of deliveries. The butcher, the baker and the fishmonger were duly summoned to the apartment, each bearing boxes of their finest wares. On that particular Christmas, we were confronted by a banquet that could easily have fed a ravenous family of ten or more. My parents' freezer would bear the burden of the celebrations well into the following spring.

I normally would have allowed myself to indulge at Christmas. But that evening, I looked at the bounty of food in front of me and felt my heart sink. I'd been suffering with digestive problems ever since my latest surgery, to the point where I'd begun to dread mealtimes. Each time I ate something, I experienced terrible acid reflux. My stomach was constantly sore and hard, as though its lining were made of concrete. Not wanting to spoil things, I attempted to down a few oysters and a couple of prawns. I also couldn't resist a slice of chocolate bûche, although, much to my mum's consternation, I declined a second serving.

I put my condition down to the mix of heavy-duty

painkillers that I'd been prescribed after the operation. The list of possible side effects made scary reading, especially since I seemed to have every one of them. At least I'd been cleared to fly as a passenger, which is how Heather and I had been able to make the trip from Biarritz. Mum and Dad retired to their room shortly after our meal.

Despite the subdued nature of our celebrations, I felt happy to be in familiar surroundings. I looked around my parents' apartment with a sense of nostalgia. I picked up a conical troca shell, a souvenir from our time in Tahiti. Instinctively I held it to my ear and imagined that I could hear the waves upon which I had surfed as a child. I set it down, and my eye was drawn to a painting of two silky-haired *vahine* women, and I smiled as I recalled the fluidity of the dance performed by these graceful island beauties. I looked over at a black-and-white photo of my father as a dashing young pilot, who smiled rakishly back at me.

"Yes, Dad, they sure were beautiful," I murmured.

That night Heather and I went for a quiet walk along the beach. With each intake of the still-warm Mediterranean air, I felt my lungs expand and begin to heal. I knew that my wife would have enjoyed a livelier Christmas, but she didn't complain.

We had spoken about how important it was for me to spend this time with Mum and Dad.

"Thanks for being here," I said.

Heather squeezed my hand in response, gazing out to the sea.

On Christmas morning, my dad joined us late for breakfast, still sporting his dressing gown and pajamas. A stark contrast to how I remembered him when he was in his fifties, in the prime of his life, cutting a fine figure in his carefully pressed American-bought chinos and button-down checked shirt. He was always clean-shaven back then, smelling of tobacco mingled with spicy aftershave. I noticed how his movements had become slow and shuffling. His swollen feet bulging out of well-worn, cozy slippers, and the cord of his dressing gown stretched to full capacity across his now considerable girth. Easing himself down into his chair, Dad let out a sigh of relief, as if getting from the bedroom to the breakfast table had been a monumental effort. As he reached out for the coffee pot, I silently noted the very prominent blue veins bulging from his gnarled hands, and the garish bruises along his arms from a recent fall, now so evident in the midday light.

That Christmas it shocked me to witness how fragile both my parents had become. How their latter years had raced by. It seemed to me that one minute, I was looking up to Mum and Dad for guidance about life, and the next they appeared to be vulnerable and seeking reassurance from me. This shift had been made all too clear when Dad picked us up from the airport a couple of days previously.

Approaching a roundabout, he'd hesitated, seemingly intimidated by the speed at which the other cars were passing in front of him.

"Go, now!" I urged, seeing a gap. But still, he'd waited, his knuckles white as his hands gripped the steering wheel. A little too late, he then slammed his foot down on the accelerator, narrowly missing an oncoming vehicle as he forced his way into the traffic. An indignant horn blared out in response, to which my dad muttered, "*Imbécile!*"

I felt my stomach lurch and quickly glanced back at Heather, who was seated in the passenger seat behind us. She returned my look in horror, but neither of us uttered a word. Who can suggest to a former captain and fighter pilot that he's no longer fit to take command of a Renault Modus?

The subject of diet was another that I knew not to broach, since food always was one of my dad's greatest pleasures. On the occasions when I'd tried, he would give a shrug and simply mutter, "I am eighty-two years old ..." In other words, *I've earned the right to live as I choose!* However, once a very active man, the truth was that my father had become increasingly sedentary in his retirement years. He preferred to view the world via the pages of *Le Figaro*, his daily newspaper.

The only hobby that remained was playing bridge, and, even then, he only did so reluctantly, accompanying my mother when she needed him to make up numbers at her regular group.

Dad's lack of exercise combined with his love of red wine and French cuisine, with its rich sauces and calorific desserts, had resulted in him piling on the kilos. But old habits die hard and, sitting at breakfast that morning, I observed him as he slathered a slice of buttery brioche with even more butter and jam. With difficulty, I bit my tongue.

Nevertheless, my father insisted that he was in good health, deflecting any questions that I might have posed by instead showing concern for me. And yet, over the Christmas period, it became clear that all was not well. For one thing, he had developed a hacking cough, which left him wheezing and gasping for breath.

"Are you okay, Dad?" I called out one morning, upon hearing him in his bedroom.

"It's nothing," he replied amid coughs. "Just a chest infection ... *(cough)* but I'm nearly over it ... *(cough)*. No need for you to *(cough)* worry, my *Coco* ... You need to look after yourself."

However, this time I refused to be simply brushed aside. Instead I badgered my dad until he agreed to see the doctor once the holidays were over. For my part, I was determined to look for something to help him regain good health. At the same time, I wanted to learn anything that could further aid my own recovery.

Back in Biarritz, I delved into more research. I was convinced that everything I was doing, namely, regular fasting and following an antiangiogenic diet, was reinforcing my immune system. But would it be enough?

I didn't kid myself into believing I was finally cancer-free. Having lived with the menacing shadow of the disease since 2003, I had grown to accept it as a constant presence in my life, one that could trip me up if I gave it the slightest opportunity. I felt that I had no choice. I had to stay vigilant and keep on top of any new developments in cancer research.

One buzzword that had come to my ears over the past few months was that of "keto." I was already aware of ketosis from my experience with fasting. However, my internet research frequently led me to a new way of eating referred to as the "ketogenic diet."

Put simply, a ketogenic diet is designed to turn the body into a fat-burning machine. It creates the effect of ketosis experienced during fasting, but without the necessity of starving yourself in the process. On a ketogenic diet, the body switches its fuel supply to run mostly on fat, rather than on the glucose of a carbohydrate-rich diet. The key to reaching ketosis is therefore to avoid consuming too many carbs. In my case, ideally no more than twenty grams per day.

An initial review of the ketogenic diet looked a little complicated, with a lot of food weighing and carb counting. I tried to explain it to Heather, whose eyes very quickly glazed over.

"So, you now want me to weigh how much chicken I put on your plate? And I'm supposed to know how many carbs are contained in a few slices of cheese?" she said in thinly disguised frustration.

"Who has the time to do that? It sounds to me like another of those fad diets. Next you'll be saying that you don't want anything but avocados for dinner!"

In truth I knew that avocados featured very heavily on the ketogenic diet, but I got her point. It wasn't going to be an easy sell, especially since she had just gotten used to the idea of my regular fasting and eating only antiangiogenic foods. I decided that I needed to speak to one of the experts behind the research, so that I could fully understand the concept, before disrupting my wife's culinary preparations yet again. One of the leading pioneer researchers in the field of treating cancer with nutrition was Professor Thomas Seyfried of Boston College, Massachusetts, who had just released a book entitled *Cancer as a Metabolic Disease*. I ordered the eye-wateringly expensive tome, which was anything but light bedtime reading. Nevertheless, Professor Seyfried's work resonated with me.

He expanded upon the findings of Nobel laureate Otto Warburg, whose work I was already familiar with, and he looked at how impaired energy metabolism could be exploited for tumor prevention and management. Seyfried argued that cancer is primarily a metabolic disease, not a genetic one, since the one trait that all cancers share is that they ferment glucose and glutamine to produce energy. Therefore, he reasoned, if the body's blood sugar level is significantly reduced to provoke the onset of ketosis, then cancer cells become unable to survive. Seyfried advocated both fasting and the ketogenic diet as effective tools in generating ketosis.

After further internet research, I managed to find a phone number for Professor Seyfried. I called the number at Boston College and was surprised to be put through to the man himself straightaway. I shared with him my story of the twelve-day fast that I'd undertaken prior to surgery on my right lung, and of my surgeon's reaction. Seyfried burst out laughing, imagining my surgeon's face as he'd stared in surprise at the tumors that he'd expected to remove during the operation, the tumors that had undergone necrosis.

Seyfried then adopted a serious tone, recounting the experience of nutrition specialist Miriam Kalamian, and her young son, Raffi.

In 2004, four-year-old Raffi was diagnosed with a brain tumor. Despite three surgeries and chemo/drug protocols, the tumor persisted. Raffi's vision, language and motor skills deteriorated. Many of his vital functions also were affected by a series of endocrine problems. Having exhausted all traditional routes, Ms. Kalamian learned of Seyfried's work on ketogenesis and reached out to him.

Under the watchful eye of a local medical team, Raffi began a ketogenic diet concurrent with a low-dose chemotherapy drug. In just three months, an MRI showed that his tumor had shrunk. Raffi then continued with a ketogenic diet as his sole therapy for a further three years.

Wanting to know more, I decided to contact Miriam Kalamian as well. Despite her personal heartache (Raffi had lost his fight with cancer in 2013, at the age of thirteen), she listened to my own experience of the disease, responding with compassionate warmth and kindness. Convinced that the ketogenic diet had prolonged her son's life, she had made it her mission to help as many other people as possible. I felt that the diet was worth a try for my own health, and I also hoped that I might convince my dad to make a few changes to his eating habits, although I knew, from past experience, that I should not feel optimistic on that front.

Before launching into the ketogenic diet and attempting to talk to my dad about its benefits, I got in touch with

American researcher and professor, Dominic D'agostino, and also French dietician and nutritionist, Magali Walkowicz. Both individuals were doing incredible work in the field of ketogenesis and health. I appreciated that they took the time to discuss their findings with me and felt even more convinced that a ketogenic approach could be a game-changer for my dad and me.

My next step was to acquire a German book that had just come out in France entitled *Le régime cétogène contre le cancer* (English translation: Combating cancer with the ketogenic diet) and was starting to generate interest in the French media. Written by three German scientists, including Professor Ulrike Kämmerer, the book was aimed at patients and contained easy-to-follow recipes and eating plans.

Leafing through the suggestions, I had an idea. It was deceptively simple, but not something that had been documented before. I would choose those foods on the ketogenic plan with the highest level of antiangiogenic properties, and combine these choices with intermittent fasting on a daily basis. Going forward, I was also determined to undertake several longer fasting periods per year. And subsequently, my own personal dietary plan was born.

———————

Over the prior months, Heather had slowly fallen in with my approach to food. It had been tough for her to begin with, since she tended to be more of a gourmet than me, loving to try new and exotic flavors. Having lived in France since 2007, she had also developed quite an appetite for French pastries — such as buttery *pain au chocolat,* or the rich, cherry-filled *Gateau Basque,* a traditional treat in our part of the world. Nevertheless, she also appreciated the benefits of switching her diet for her own health. Her morning croissant routine disappeared. Breakfasts gradually merged into brunches, and our three meals per day became replaced by just two.

As I was now on sick leave, and Heather worked from home, it was much easier for us to make these changes to our diet than it would have been if either of us was working in an office. We therefore got into the habit of eating brunch at around midday. This would typically include salad, salmon, avocado, poached eggs, tomatoes and some hard goat cheese. In order to satisfy our desire for sweetness, we would finish with some berries (raspberries, strawberries and blueberries, depending upon seasonal availability) and almonds.

Our evening meal was eaten no later than 8:00 p.m. and was usually something simple such as grilled vegetables and chicken or fish. We indulged in a glass of red wine once a week. The majority of these foods had the highest levels of antiangiogenic response and were also in keeping with the ketogenic diet. We didn't weigh our food portions, but started to use smaller plates to ensure that we didn't overeat.

During the day, I got into the habit of regularly testing my level of ketosis to ascertain whether I was on track. To this end, I purchased a simple testing kit, which I easily found at my local pharmacy. The procedure involved placing the test end of the paper strip into my urine, which I collected in a clean, dry receptacle. I then waited fifteen seconds. The urine strips had a color chart that measured ketone bodies, ranging from trace quantities to large amounts. Higher levels of ketone were indicated by a deep purple color. However, the ideal state was a result in the mid-range and dark pink in color. I found it useful to keep a record of my ketone levels and to note any changes that showed up in relation to specific foods that I had eaten. My latest combined dietary approach seemed to be working, since the stomach problems lessened and eventually disappeared. I was excited to share the results with my dad, convinced that he and Mum would benefit from my findings. Sadly, I didn't get the chance to do so.

It was not long after Christmas that my world was given another brutal knock. Seeing my parents' number appear on my ringing phone, I had expected to pick up and hear my mum's voice on the line. She often called in the early evening to see how our day had been, or perhaps to recommend a program on television. However, it was not my mum, but Valerie's voice on the line, and I knew that something was wrong.

Valerie had worked for my parents for many years, initially helping out during the week with shopping and cleaning. Later, her role had transitioned into that of a care-giver, showing up every day to ensure that they took their medication and dressing the leg ulcers, to which they were both prone. Valerie told me that my father had fallen two days previously, sustaining a knock to the head. Always a proud man, Dad hadn't wanted anyone to know.

"Let me speak to him," I'd said, assuming that we'd have our usual chat, and that he'd tell me the women were fussing over nothing. Instead, our brief conversation revealed the extent of my dad's difficulties. Struggling to string a coherent sentence together, he'd appeared vague and distant—a far cry from his usual eloquence and reputation as a great raconteur. With a growing sense of alarm, I knew this was a clear signal he needed medical help.

CHAPTER 15

Dad

IN ANGUISH I WATCHED via FaceTime as two burly ambulance workers eased my father into a wheelchair. He sat motionless and stared back at me, his startled, pale blue eyes reflecting an inner turmoil.

"It's okay, Dad," I reassured, speaking over FaceTime via a phone that was being held up for him. "I'm coming soon."

Dad nodded and waved his hand in a detached fashion. He didn't appear to understand what was happening. It shocked me to see him like that.

Mum stood nearby, hunched over the walker with which she was steadying herself. Wherever my dad went, she was determined to follow. She seemed smaller than usual, as if dwarfed by the enormity of Dad's deteriorating health. He had always been her rock, her protector. She'd railed against any suggestion of calling the ambulance, fearing that he wouldn't come home again. In the end she'd accepted that he needed help.

Two days after Dad was admitted to the hospital, I received a call from my brother, Jean-Yves, who relayed the news that I'd been dreading. Tests had revealed that our father's body was riddled with tumors. Originating in the lungs, they had spread to the brain, abdomen and prostate.

This hit me hard. Though, I suppose, on a subconscious level, I'd been expecting it. That cough over Christmas was similar to the one I'd had before my own diagnosis each time. And, unlike me, my dad had smoked for years. Back when he was in the prime of his aviation career, it seemed everyone smoked. Though it's hard to imagine today, when smoking on planes is strictly forbidden, I've seen photos of him in the cockpit with his pipe dangling from his mouth. He'd finally given up smoking when he was in his late sixties, but now he was paying the price.

After my call with Jean-Yves, I hopped on a flight and headed straight to the hospital. There, I was joined by my brother and also my sister, Taina, who had made the long journey from her home in Reunion Island upon hearing the news. Dad was to be kept in the hospital for observation for a couple of weeks while he underwent further tests.

At one point I found myself alone with my father, sitting in companionable silence. He was breathing with the aid of oxygen tubes fed into his nose and found it difficult to speak. Nevertheless, he reached out his hand and nudged my wrist, urging me to come closer to him. I put my ear next to his mouth.

"It's time for you to take this, my son," he rasped.

I looked down and saw that his right hand was unnaturally bare. He'd managed to twist the heavy gold ring off his swollen third finger and was proffering it to me. It was the ring he'd received after graduating from the United States Air Force in 1953. I'd always known that it would one day be mine. As a young boy, I had coveted that special piece of jewelry and all that it represented. No amount of money could buy that ring. It had to be earned.

I can't remember ever seeing my father without those wings of the American eagle and US Air Force. By relinquishing his precious ring to my care, he was effectively passing the baton on to me. From one pilot to the next. It was now my duty to guide our family through whatever the future held in store for us, through sunshine and storms.

"Look after your mum," he'd whispered. I took the ring and slipped it loosely onto my own finger, a lump rising in my throat.

"It's not over yet, Dad," I said. "I'll wear it for you until you're better."

He looked at me and smiled.

Over the days that followed, my siblings and I began to notify members of our extended family, and also Dad's closest friends, of his deteriorating health. Many came to visit him in the hospital, which lifted his spirits a bit. However, there was one call that only I, and I alone, could make. It was one that I had been putting off, since I knew it would have a devastating impact on me too. With a heavy heart I touched the FaceTime icon on my phone, secretly hoping that no one would answer.

"Hey, bro!" came the familiar carefree voice, accompanied by the smiling, tanned face of my childhood friend, Paul, in Tahiti. "What's up?!"

I gulped and attempted to hold it together, trying to find the words to tell him about Dad. I was aware that the news would break my friend's heart. Just before I spoke, Paul had looked so happy and relaxed. Now in his mid-fifties, with sun-bleached hair, Paul would still surf whenever he got the chance. He had lost none of the easygoing demeanor of someone who spends much of his life near the ocean.

He and my father shared a special bond, since it was Dad who'd stepped in when Paul had gone off the rails in his late teens. At the time, he'd been turning into a beach bum, with little interest in anything other than partying. Now a pilot for Air Tahiti Nui, it was to my father that he owed his career. My dad had treated Paul like a son, getting him back on the straight and narrow and encouraging him to study for his flying license.

In the end I simply said, "It's Dad ... he's got cancer. It's all over the place."

I've never seen anyone look more shattered than Paul did that day.

"Let me speak to him," he replied, his voice cracking.

I then re-entered the hospital room and handed the phone to my dad, before stepping out once more so the two could speak in private. I don't know exactly what was said but, upon returning to my father's bedside, I could see my friend's grief-stricken face. I knew that they had said their goodbyes.

Not long after, the oncologist gathered me and my siblings together. He informed us that Dad's condition was too far advanced to attempt anything other than palliative care. It would be a matter of weeks, he told us. Together we made the decision to take our father home. We knew, since nothing more could be done for him from a medical point of view, he would prefer to spend his last days surrounded by the love of his family. My father's happiest times had been spent in Tahiti, near the ocean, on an island fragrant with tiaré-infused Monoi oil and lush with vegetation. There was no way that we would let him die in a sterile hospital environment, with clinical white walls and the smell of antiseptic.

What followed were some of the toughest moments of my life. The immediate family gathered together at my parents' home. My son flew in from Sydney to be with his grandfather. Kelly came to help too.

The bedroom that my mother and father had shared for so many years was transformed into a mini hospital ward. It was equipped with all the necessary medical paraphernalia, bandages, syringes, oxygen bottles ... The entire family had to quickly learn how everything worked. We had assumed the responsibility of providing my father with round-the-clock care and had to know what to do in case of an emergency. Two nurses also came to help out three times per day but, it was otherwise left up to us, the family.

With all the family assembled, Dad's health took a

nosedive. It was as though my father had been hanging on to see everyone one last time. We took turns to be on standby, with someone staying awake each night in case he needed anything. Kelly and Jeff demonstrated a degree of courage and maturity beyond anything I could have imagined that they possessed. At one point, they together changed their grandfather's soiled adult nappy. They did so without complaint.

There were times when we truly felt out of our depth. On one occasion, in particular, my father was fighting for breath, and we were unable to stabilize him. Traumatized by the look of panic on Dad's face, I called the emergency services in the middle of the night. A team of four or five men arrived in short order and rushed to Dad's side. Some twenty minutes had passed before they were able to adjust the equipment and make Dad comfortable again. Before leaving, the head of the team took me aside.

"What you are doing as a family is incredible," he marveled, his eyes wet with emotion. "You wouldn't believe how many people just leave their elderly relatives to die alone in the hospital."

His words meant a lot to me, since at times I felt our efforts were not enough, and I feared that we were failing my dad. But, in my heart, I knew we were doing the best that we could.

Dad and I had our talks every day, just the two of us. Sometimes they were brief because he needed to rest, but he always called me back to his room, and we resumed from where he had left off. He wore a transparent oxygen mask that covered his entire nose and mouth, making it difficult to hear what he was saying, yet we recalled our happy years spent in Tahiti, and we talked about those special things only pilots witness, such as the magnificent spectacle of the northern lights as seen from the cockpit at night.

My dad loved the stars. As a pilot of the old school, he could navigate by them, something us new generation of pilots never learned. Aviation was his life, and he'd loved every minute of it, crossing the oceans from continent to continent, landing in Sydney, Los Angeles, San Francisco, New York … he truly had experienced the golden era of flying.

Since I was the oldest of his children, Dad sought my reassurance that everything was in order for my mother, his wife of fifty years. He needed to know that, whatever happened, she would be taken care of. I repeated the promise that I had made when he gave me his ring. However, his concern hadn't been necessary, as he had seen to it that all of the required paperwork was done long before he became ill.

As the days passed, it became abundantly clear that Dad was getting into greater difficulty. His lungs were becoming saturated with fluid, and his breathing was growing worse. It was emotionally painful for everyone involved. There came a time when the oxygen was no longer sufficient to make Dad feel comfortable. He was slowly drowning in his own fluid. That's when the nurse told me what to expect as the end approached, so that I could prepare myself as much as possible.

Dad had always spoken openly to me throughout his life, and one of the things he shared was that his biggest fear had been to die by drowning. Knowing what was going on with his lungs, I was resolved that I would not allow this to be his fate.

His lesser organs were shutting down to protect the heart and brain. The nurse told me that eventually his kidney would stop functioning, and the fluid levels would rise, first in his arms and legs, and then it would further saturate his lungs, effectively causing him to drown. There was no way I was going to let this happen.

After he'd been home for about three weeks, each day his breathing became increasingly labored. It was horrific to witness. The nurse took me aside and told me that he could be administered a special medication to ease him into a restful sleep when he was close to the end.

The hardest day of my life came one evening when my dad's battle for breath was becoming desperate. I was alone in the room with him at the time when he summoned all of his remaining strength to signal me to approach the bed, and then whispered the words that I will never forget.

"I want to sleep now."

I gazed into his still piercingly blue eyes, and his meaning was clear. However, I needed to be sure, so I got very close to his ear and asked him directly.

He nodded, repeating, "I just want to sleep now."

I swallowed hard, knowing that this was no time to break down. After so many years of being a pillar of strength for us all, my father needed me to be strong for him, for my mum, and everyone else. I called the nurse, who agreed that she would administer the medication of which we had already spoken. There was no way I would allow my father to die by drowning.

Nobody wanted to accept it, but we all knew that my dad's time had come. We all gathered around him. Although he was weak, we took pictures of Dad with each of us. The atmosphere was surreal as we celebrated this special man, an adored husband, father and grandfather, doing our best to remain in the present moment, as every second that remained was so precious. And yet, I was all too aware that, some thirty minutes later, life would never be the same again. My beloved father would be no more.

The final moments of my dad's life were beautiful. As he drifted off to an eternal sleep, Tahitian music played softly in the background. The sounds of these enchanting islands were the last that he heard. He was surrounded by the love of his family, and he left this world at peace, knowing that his job was complete.

I knew that I would miss my father for the rest of my life, yet I also felt proud of what we as a family had done for him. He had been emotionally supported by each of us and was aware of and acknowledged our presence every day. In his more lucid moments, he would say to me, "I have a fantastic family ... what a wonderful life it's been."

In my eyes, my father will always be my hero and, feeling the weight of his gold ring on my finger, as these words are written, I know he will always be with me when I am up there, flying among the stars. As I said my own personal farewell, I vowed that I would one day get back in the cockpit. I would do it for my father, Jacques Trochon, for the person who gave me life and made me the man I am today.

CHAPTER 16

A Parting Gift

THE EARLY EVENING weather was mild and infused with the promise of summer—my first summer without Dad. His funeral had taken place the day before, and I missed him so much my bones hurt. I couldn't imagine a time when the crushing grief might fade. Alone, I sat on the weathered wooden bench overlooking the beach near my parents' apartment. It had been one of my father's favorite spots in his latter years. I took a little comfort in the knowledge that his eyes had scanned this same horizon. It hadn't been so very long ago. And now he was gone.

Overhead, a flock of seagulls swooped across the bay, their raucous squawking appeared to mock my own chorus of coughing fits. I'd been coughing with increasing regularity over the past few days. I'd ignored it at first, since it started when Dad died a little more than a week prior. I'd put it down to stress. But at this point, I became concerned. In recent years, coughing had been a harbinger of bad news, an indicator of malignant nodules invading my lungs.

In an attempt to breathe normally, I stood up, stretched and made my way down to the beach. Taking greedy gulps of sea air, I began to sense my body relax. The ocean has always had this effect on me. It gives me the feeling of being centered, taking me back to my happy childhood in Polynesia. I picked up a pebble that had washed up on the sand. For a moment I held it in my palm, enjoying its smoothness and warmth against my skin. And then, with a practiced aim, I sent it skipping across the glassy blue of the Mediterranean. It was a simple gesture, but with it, I also felt myself letting go. Finally releasing the emotions I'd tried so hard to control. With no one around to witness my pain, I allowed tears to stream down my face.

I stayed on the beach for some time after that, feeling drained but also soothed by the gentle lapping of the water. As I sat looking out at the myriad of greens and blues in front of me, I was reminded of a recent conversation I'd had with my father's nurse.

It had been a couple of weeks before Dad's death. His nurse had spoken to me about an innovative product called NaturaBlue that she'd started to use on her patients, and they saw positive results. It was produced by the company Natura4Ever.[3] The product in question was a concentrated blue liquid, rich in something called phycocyanin, which is extracted from spirulina.

I was familiar with the microalgae known as spirulina, a powerful natural antioxidant and anti-inflammatory agent, which I had been taking in either powder or tablet form whenever I'd wanted to give my immune system a boost. However, the nurse explained to me that phycocyanin (a cyan blue pigment specific to spirulina) stimulates the formation of red and white blood cells necessary for a healthy organism. Looking at the ocean in front of me, I thought once more of the product. It had been too late for my father, but maybe it could help me. I felt it was worth a try. I returned to my parents' apartment and went to look for the bottle of the precious pigment that the nurse had recommended.

MY NEW BLUE-GREEN REGIME

As with any new health approach, I carried out my research seriously before trying it. I again scoured the internet, determined to learn everything about spirulina and phycocyanin. What I discovered set me off on a path that would change the course of my life.

Before I write about my own protocol, I would like to share some fascinating information about the product that became an essential part of my everyday diet following my father's death.

Spirulina is a blue-green microalgae, a so-called cyanobacteria, one of the largest and most important groups of bacteria on Earth. Cyanobacteria are classified as bacteria because their genetic material is not organized in a membrane-bound nucleus. Unlike other bacteria, they contain chlorophyll and use the sun as an energy source, in the way plants and algae do.

Cyanobacteria were the first photosynthetic life forms on our planet. By creating an atmospheric oxygen content close to today's level, they enabled other life forms to evolve. Since then, these microalgae have helped regulate our planet's biosphere. Cyanobacteria are therefore considered to be at the origin of life, the original link in the food chain, nourishing zooplankton, fish, large marine mammals and, ultimately, the human race. They are believed to have come into being some three and a half billion years ago, according to traces found in stromatolites in South Africa and Australia.

During my research I learned that there are some 1,500 species of cyanobacteria in existence, only thirty-six of which are edible. Of those that are edible, spirulina is unique in its ability to provide for the majority of the human body's nutritional requirements.

Spirulina is packed full of vital nutrients, including vitamins A, E and B, as well as a whole host of minerals such as calcium, magnesium, zinc, selenium and, of course, the pigment phycocyanin. Further reading on the subject revealed that spirulina has a considerably higher concentration of nutrients compared to other foods. I was amazed that just a few tablespoons of spirulina could provide such nutritional benefits.

For example, gram for gram:

Spirulina has 3900 percent more **beta-carotene** than carrot

2300 percent more **iron** than spinach

300 percent more **calcium** than whole milk, and

375 percent more **protein** than tofu and 200 percent more than meat.

Spirulina, in its natural algae form, can be found in warm, alkaline lakes and ponds. In addition to its value as a food source, what makes spirulina so special is its ability to absorb heavy metals and toxins from its environment. It is able to do so on account of its soft cell walls, which make it highly efficient in absorbing the toxic substances in our bodies. Once toxins are absorbed, our bodies are able to eliminate them through the regular process of digestion. However, on account of this toxin absorption property, it is essential to consume only spirulina that has originated from a clean source.

I also learned that spirulina isn't only popular in Europe. Around the globe, the top curators of health and health recommendations have recognized spirulina for its important contribution to physical wellbeing. In 1974, the United Nations World Food Conference announced that spirulina is "the most ideal food for mankind." One of the most profound examples of the use of spirulina for good health is that of the 1986 Chernobyl disaster. Following the devastating accident at the nuclear plant, many exposed children became stricken with chronic radiation sickness and elevated Immunoglobulin E (IgE) levels, as well as testing positive for high allergy sensitivity. After being administered roughly five grams (0.18 ounces) of spirulina per day for forty-five days, the children's IgE levels and allergic sensitivities were restored back to normal.

Throughout the late 1980s and early '90s, both NASA and the European Space Agency proposed spirulina as one of the primary foods to be cultivated during long-term space missions.

On June 8, 1993, the United Nations World Health Organization (WHO) declared, "Spirulina represents an interesting food for multiple reasons, for example, it is rich in iron and protein and is able to be administered to children without any risk."

In 2003, the Intergovernmental Institution for the use of Micro-algae Spirulina Against Malnutrition was formed and, in 2008, the UN Food and Agriculture Organization (FAO) report on spirulina stated that there exists "a need for both national governments and inter-governmental organizations to re-evaluate the potential of spirulina to fulfill both their own food security needs, as well as a tool for their overseas development emergency response efforts."

In the face of so much evidence, I decided to add a daily dose of the microalgae to my healthy living approach, alongside the two pillars of an antiangiogenic and a keto diet, combined with the third—regular bouts of fasting. I continued to take spirulina in dry form, but added a high dose of liquid phycocyanin (4 x 16 ml or 0.5 fluid ounces per day). I mixed the two supplements together in a glass of water.

Over a period of two weeks I noticed that my cough had begun to subside. At one point, I coughed up some black matter that looked like dried blood. I wondered if it could be the residue of an old tumor. Some thirteen days after taking this high dose of phyco-spirulina at regular intervals, my cough disappeared completely. I also felt better than I had in weeks. I decided then to make spirulina the fourth pillar in my anticancer regimen.

On a spiritual level, I felt as if this new form of phyco-spirulina had come into my life as a parting gift from my father. Even though it had been too late to save his life, the fact that his nurse had introduced it to me meant that it could potentially help to save my own.

I continued to experience many dark moments in the weeks following my father's funeral. Nevertheless, I had promised him that I would assume his position as head of the family and take care of everyone after he'd gone. To do this, I had to be in good health. This was not the time to cave in to depression and allow cancer to defeat me. Knowing how proud my father would have been of me served as further motivation to heal completely and once again take command from the left seat in the cockpit. I also felt that up there in the sky among the stars was the one place that I might truly be aware of his presence again. It had been six months since my last operation. The time had come to go for another scan.

FIT TO FLY

The results were better than I'd ever dared to hope: I was given the all-clear!

For the first time in this long period of desperate sadness and despair, I finally felt I might be turning a corner. Maybe, just maybe, I would be able to prove to the Air France medical team that I was fit to fly again. However, I didn't want to take any chances and decided to give myself more time to heal my mind, body and soul. For the remainder of the year, everything I did was aimed at my continued recovery. I was aware that life wasn't much fun for Heather during this time, since my major preoccupation was cancer research and how I could apply it to my own health. Fortunately, my wife continued to be very supportive. She had already adopted some of my approaches, such as diet and intermittent fasting, and she had started taking NaturaBlue as well. Although a little skeptical at first, she noticed benefits for her own health and said that she felt less tired. Indeed, we both had a renewed sense of optimism as we looked to the future.

During this period, I continued to undergo a scan every three months, and each one came back clear. Dr. Escudier, who had prepared me for the worst a few months prior, had been expecting to see a new growth of cancer cells. Though perplexed, he was delighted for me. I had yet to fully convince him of the benefits of fasting, spirulina or being able to "eat to beat" cancer, but he had begun to listen with interest when I told him about my latest findings. Personally, I had no doubt that my ability to defy the odds was due to my four-pillared approach. I also knew that I would continue to practice it for the rest of my life.

The day that I'd much longed for—but barely dared hope to see—finally arrived. In February 2016, I was given the "okay" by the civil aviation medical authorities. The time had come to reclaim my wings! I knew that I would be supervised until the instructors were completely satisfied that I'd met all the rigorous demands of the job, but I was one step closer to fulfilling my dream of wearing my captain's stripes again. In so doing, I would be flying for my dad, my mum, my kids, Heather, and for everyone who had supported me throughout those difficult years. I also would be flying for other cancer sufferers.

Back then, many of my colleagues at Air France knew about my illness. Some were undergoing their own battles against cancer, while others watched helplessly as loved ones were diagnosed. Knowing how difficult it can be in the face of cancer to keep a sense of optimism, my aim was to show all of them that it is possible to fight this disease, that there is life after cancer and a reason to hope.

CHAPTER 17

Flying High Again

"CLEAR FOR TAKEOFF 26 R," came the control tower announcement.

"Clear for takeoff 26 R," my co-pilot acknowledged.

"Takeoff," I confirmed.

"Thrust set," responded my co-pilot. "80 knots."

"Check," I confirmed.

With an acceleration of speed, we thundered down the runway.

"Rotate," called out my co-pilot.

I rotated the plane and, a split second later, we were airborne into a cloudless sky. It was a perfect takeoff on a perfect day in Paris—the kind of day that made me feel privileged to be a pilot. And that was the very moment when things started to go wrong.

On came the master warning lights, flashing an angry red on the screen in front of me. Accompanying them, an alarm blared out in the cockpit. Simultaneously, an emergency message appeared before my eyes: "Engine fire."

Adrenalin pulsated through my body as we ascended to 400 feet. I needed to ensure that we had sufficient height above ground before turning on the autopilot. Once at the required altitude, I was able to activate the emergency steps, all the time keeping a cool head. Years of training had prepared me for moments like this.

"Engine fire procedure," I ordered.

Only when I had the situation under control did I make my announcement to the tower.

"May Day! May Day! May Day!" I called out over the mic.

"Air France 126. Engine fire! Standby!"

A calm voice then came from behind me. I was taken by surprise, since I had been so engrossed in handling the emergency. It was the voice of my instructor.

"Nice execution, Jean-Jacques. Let's stop for a ten-minute tea break, boys!"

I'd spent many weeks preparing to go into the simulator again. It had been a challenge to study once more after such a long period of absence. Often I'd felt as though I was drowning in paperwork. Air France continually sent me updated procedures with new pages, where I had to remove the obsolete sections from umpteen files and replace them with the latest ones. (Air France had yet to digitalize its training manuals back then.) It was easy to lose track of things. There were times I became so frustrated trying to keep it all organized, I'd throw my documents aside in sheer despair.

Yet, I knew that even to be given the opportunity to fly again was like winning millions in the lottery. Literally. The chances of it happening had felt equally as remote. Upon being diagnosed with stage four cancer, I'd had the impression that, as a pilot, I would be written off. There was that certain look on my co-worker's faces, a mixture of pity and awkwardness when they saw me and didn't know what to say. I could tell no one imagined that I would one day be back in the cockpit. It was unthinkable that anyone would make the return after stage four cancer. And yet, I wanted to prove everyone wrong.

In February 2016, I'd gotten the all-clear from the aviation medical board that I was fit to fly. However, actually getting through the grueling simulator sessions and then being given that crucial all-clear to captain a commercial flight was quite another matter. I needn't have worried.

My Air France colleagues were beyond supportive. Other captains vied with one another to be my instructor. By the third simulator session, I'd regained my confidence to the point that I felt ready for the real thing.

My urgency to get back in the hot seat had been further bolstered by a surprise call from my oncologist and now-friend, Bernard Escudier. Shortly before my simulator training began, he informed me of a trip he'd booked to South Africa where he'd be speaking at a couple of conferences and then planned to holiday in Cape Town, accompanied by his wife.

The timing was perfect. I was determined to be the one to captain Bernard's South African flight. What better way to show him that I'd beaten the disease which, not so long ago, he had believed would prematurely end my life?

Buoyed by my success in the simulators, I put in a request for the Cape Town flight. Though Cape Town was a much-coveted destination, none of my colleagues bid against me after my absence of two years. Everyone knew how much South Africa meant to me, and they wanted me to go as much as I did.

My passion for Springboks rugby was common knowledge. I was also the one who'd opened the route when Air France first flew the Boeing 777 there in October 2011, just before I'd experienced my first recurrence of cancer. It would feel so special to be back on African soil. I fantasized that perhaps, if conditions were right, I could request a special approach, enabling me to fly the plane over Table Mountain — the famous flat-topped mountain with a majestic beauty that provides a stunning backdrop to the Cape Town skyline.

But all that was still ahead of me. First, I had to get those stripes back on my shoulders again.

My control flight was scheduled to New York at the beginning of March. This flight would determine, once again, whether or not I'd earn my stripes. For me, it felt like business as usual. I had been out of the loop for two years, but I knew the drill by heart. The outward leg went smoothly. I then spent twenty-four hours resting in the Big Apple before heading back to Paris.

With things going well on the return, at one point, my instructor took a brief nap in the seat beside me. I chose this moment to whisper a few words to my father.

"I'm here, Dad. Can you see me?"

I positioned his gold graduation ring toward the cockpit window, making sure the angle was just right. Illuminated by panels of instruments, I wanted the ring to point to the stars. We'd spoken of the stars often during many intimate conversations in my dad's final few weeks. Some people might have questioned my sanity at that point, but I truly felt Dad's presence up there.

Having taken off from JFK airport earlier that evening, we were nearing Charles de Gaulle. I was just a couple of hours away from being given the green light to fly again, to once more be able wear the captain's insignia that I had worked all of my professional life to achieve. When we touched down in Paris, my instructor turned to me and smiled. He then shook my hand as he said the two words that I had been longing to hear, "Welcome back."

Much to my delight, my request to fly to Cape Town was granted. On March 10, 2016, I undertook my first flight back as captain. Heather joined me for this special trip, and even sat behind me in the cockpit during takeoff. I admit, I barely noticed her as I carried out my pre-flight checklist. I was completely in the zone and concentrated all of my energy on the job at hand. It was only once we were airborne that I turned to look at her and saw the tears in her eyes. We'd been through some difficult times together. There had been several moments when we had both wondered if this day would ever come.

I gave my wife a reassuring smile.

"Why don't you go and take your seat in the cabin," I said, knowing that a comfortable, and well-deserved, business class seat awaited her.

The ten-hour flight ran smoothly. It was around midday on a gloriously sunny morning as we neared the Mother City, as Cape Town is lovingly nicknamed by the country's inhabitants. I talked to the controllers, taking on the South African accent into which I naturally slip when I speak with the locals.

"Hello, Cape Town approach," I said.

"Hello Air France 864," crackled the reply, the accent heavy with that familiar clipped English.

"Hi guys, good to be back!" I replied. "Great weather today. Requesting to fly over Table Mountain."

"With pleasure. All good for today. Fly Robben Island, heading 180. And you're clear for a visual approach, left downwind. Runway 01. Descent to 5000."

"*Lekker*," I replied in delight. "Thanks, guys!" I then made a passenger announcement.

"Well folks, we're going to be flying over Table Mountain in a few seconds. Prepare your cameras. It's going to be a good one."

And then we passed over that most iconic of landmarks at

minimum security altitude, where you could almost see the color of the eyes of anyone who happened to be looking up at the plane. To the west lay Lion's Head, so called on account of its sphinx-like profile. And there, shimmering below me, was Kommetjie Bay. How many times had I surfed in those waters? So many memories came flooding in. It was there that I'd once broke a rib during a particularly spectacular wipeout. To this day, my left rib still sticks out as a reminder of the ocean's supreme power.

After landing, I was given a hero's welcome by the Air France team. All the familiar faces were present, including Paul, head of ground staff, and the indomitable Maria in her official blue trouser suit, her blonde hair scraped into a *chignon*.

"Welcome back, Captain Trochon."

"Howzit, JJ!"

"*Sawubona!*"

I responded to each greeting with a smile.

Everyone seemed to be aware of my battle, and they each hugged me warmly — so many people of the different ethnicities that make up this rainbow nation. With each step I took away from the airport, I could sense my body relaxing. It felt good to be back on familiar territory.

It was the same story when we arrived at our hotel, Crystal Towers. Over the years I had built up a close relationship with the team there too. I was personally greeted by the hotel manager and her staff, all of whom wore huge smiles. At this point I could feel the tiredness and emotion taking over, and I had to fight to keep my composure. Next I was being ushered into a side room by one of the Crystal Tower employees.

"Hey guys ... what's going on?!" I said, since this was not the normal routine upon arriving at a hotel. I had no idea that while I had been kept busy, talking to the hotel manager, the rest of my crew, along with Heather, had secretly gathered in this side room and were waiting for me.

Usually everyone is so exhausted after the flight that they can't wait to head to their rooms and hit the sack. I'd assumed that was where everyone had gone. Instead, I was confronted by a group of tired but beaming faces. It was then that I noticed the glasses of champagne in their hands. My crew were gathered around a table with a beautifully decorated cake at the center. It featured an airplane, the red, white and blue of the French flag, and the message:

"Captain Trochon, *nous sommes très ravi que vous etes de retour.*" (sic.)

(Captain Trochon, we are delighted to have you back)

Words failed me, as tears took their place. It had been a long journey to get there, but more than worth the struggle.

———

The festivities continued the next day. I'd arranged to hold a *braii*, as South Africans refer to a barbecue, at the house of some very dear friends. My hosts, Wilf and Wendy, are like my second parents. I first got to know Wilf, a former high court judge, when I'd spent time in Cape Town as a young pilot. Wilf and I used to go running together and quickly grew to like and respect each other as friends. I was highly touched that he and Wendy so readily agreed to open up their home to me when I'd suggested holding a small gathering. It would be my way of giving thanks to those South Africans who had supported me over the years. Around forty people showed up, including some of my friends from SA Rugby and Air France.

Wilf and Wendy live in a beautiful house in the residential suburb of Tokai, in the foothills of Constantiaberg. Their sprawling home is filled with art and books, and has been the scene of many great parties. Since I'd often stayed there when I visited Cape Town, I knew that it would provide the perfect location for my own small celebration.

The weather was kind to us on the evening of the *braii*, enabling my guests to eat outside beneath a vine-draped pergola. Sipping chilled South African wine, I reveled in the lushness of our surroundings. A keen gardener, Wendy had nurtured an oasis that is also home to a host of wild birds, among which were families of guinea fowl strutting around the garden like a bunch of mini-Mick Jaggers, and also hadeda, a species of ibis named on account of their raucous call (*ha ha hadeda*).

Once we had enjoyed a ketogenic feast of healthy salads and grilled meats, I took a moment to officially introduce my very special guest, Doctor Bernard Escudier, along with his wife, Estelle. It was such a privilege to be able to honor the man who had been at my side for much of my cancer journey.

I then gave a short speech during which I explained to everyone just how I had tackled my cancer. For many of the assembled, it was the first time they learned the full details of what I had undergone. Until then, I'd relayed information on my condition and progress updates in brief WhatsApp messages. Many hadn't realized the extent of my ongoing battle.

On that evening, in the golden glow of a late South African summer, I spoke for the first time about my four pillars of health: 1) an antiangiogenic, 2) a ketogenic diet, 3) fasting and 4) spirulina. I also explained how the surgeon had removed my lung from my body during the last two operations, deflating it and manually feeling for tumors. Despite the gasps, I spared my friends nothing because I wanted to drive home the importance of looking after their own health.

I offered the latest statistics of how, within ten to fifteen years, one in two people will have some form of cancer. I looked around at my guests and could see their shocked expressions, no doubt imagining themselves in my situation.

Throughout my speech I was also aware of Bernard's eyes glancing from face to face, observing the impact that my words were having. It was at that point that I realized a significant change had taken place in the way my oncologist viewed both my approach to the disease and me.

Two days later, I welcomed Bernard and his wife on board my flight. My oncologist was equally elated as I at the change in my circumstances. After breaking the terrible news of my stage four cancer to me, he'd believed he would also have to prepare me for the worst. He certainly never expected to be a passenger on one of my flights a little over two years later.

During the course of the flight, I had some time to speak with Bernard in private. He'd been quite skeptical about my fasting routine, my daily intake of spirulina and my very specific approach to diet. However, he was now forced to admit that I might well be on to something. After initially telling me that fasting was *"bon pour la ligne"* (good for the silhouette), he was now interested to know more, asking me to send him information upon our return to France. Furthermore, he asked me if I would speak at an annual kidney cancer conference that he organized in Paris. Naturally I accepted with pleasure, all too keen to help other people in my position.

"We doctors don't have all the answers," he smiled. "Maybe you have discovered something we need to learn."

CHAPTER 18

The Start of a Revolution

THE THIRTEENTH OF APRIL, 2016, was not the first time that I'd attended the patient meeting of A.R.Tu.R., a kidney cancer research association, in Paris. Back in 2013, I had sat as an anxious audience member, hoping in vain to hear about a revolutionary new cancer treatment that might save my life. I'd left feeling despondent and powerless, as none of the presenters had a single proven cancer therapy to share. However, this time would be different, since this time I was not there as a regular attendee. Bernard Escudier, president of A.R.Tu.R., had invited me as a speaker, and I would be sharing a message that I believed would buoy the audience with a concrete reason for hope.

Heather and I sat in that packed auditorium listening to

Bernard address approximately three hundred kidney cancer patients and a few doctors. At this, the tenth annual meeting, I looked around and saw that each member of the audience was hanging on Bernard's every word, keen to hear some positive news about advances in cancer treatments. This was my circle, a group of people of various ages, ethnicities and genders, all brought together by the common denominator of our disease. It wasn't a group to which I had chosen to belong, but there was a degree of comfort in knowing that we were all in the same boat, albeit at different stages of our journeys.

Bernard's talk reviewed the evolution of treatments over the past ten years and shared insight on new ones that were still in clinical trials but showed promise for future use on patients. He also spoke about antiangiogenic treatments, the kind that he'd proposed to me prior to my surgery in 2014. However, he concluded by saying that none of these treatments had resulted in a complete remission of metastatic kidney cancer. Just like the last time I'd attended in 2013, Bernard's message was sobering for all those present.

His presentation was followed by a lively Q&A session, during which one topic was raised repeatedly: fasting.

"We're starting to hear about how fasting could provide support for cancer treatments," said one audience member. "Why aren't we being told about this?"

Bernard appeared surprised and paused momentarily. Clearly, he had not expected this type of question.

"I'm not the right person to respond to this," he said. "I cannot discuss something on which I am not an expert." He then surprised me by continuing. "There is someone more qualified than myself to talk about fasting. Please join me in welcoming Jean-Jacques Trochon to the stage."

Listed on the program under the title "patient testimonial," I was taken aback by Bernard's introduction, since I hadn't anticipated being set up as an expert on the subject. Nevertheless, I set aside my apprehension and took to the stage amid the audience's polite, yet restrained applause.

"Hello, ladies and gentlemen. My name is Jean-Jacques Trochon. I am an airline captain with Air France and, since 2003, I have been battling kidney cancer ..."

Speaking at the meeting proved to be a turning point for me. It was the first time I had talked about my protocol to a large audience, and the first time I had openly discussed my own experience of so-called alternative approaches, which many doctors had considered to be dubious science at best. Even today, mention the word "fasting" and many physicians and nurses will raise their eyebrows and shake their heads. But there I was, sharing this information on stage at the invitation of one of the world's most respected oncologists!

With so much information to share, I exceeded my allotted twenty minutes by a further ten. I could have continued for much longer, had it not been time for the lunch break. Once I had finally finished, Bernard took to the stage once more and thanked me.

Everyone in that packed auditorium got to their feet and gave me a standing ovation that seemed to last forever. It felt incredible. I believe they saw me as a cancer survivor, and I had given them hope that they, too, could take charge of their health.

During the break I found myself surrounded by a group of passionate individuals, all wanting my advice on how to fast, what kind of spirulina to take, where to find out about antiangiogenic foods and how to follow a ketogenic diet. I had been totally unprepared for this kind of attention and initially found it stressful. I realized that many of those looking to me for help were already very sick. Some told me that the medical system was failing them, and that they believed maybe I had discovered a magic cure. I felt the weight of this enormous responsibility, but I listened to everybody's story and advised each person as best I could.

At one point I looked up and scanned the room to try to locate Heather. She was on the opposite side, balancing a plate of salad from the buffet while trying to answer questions and take down email addresses, so she could forward information to those who requested it. I felt proud of my wife and her nonstop support. Neither of us expected our lives to go down this path when we married in 2008, and yet she has never once complained.

Seeing the looks of desperation on the faces of some of those who told me their stories made me want to help in any way I could. I gave my phone number to anyone who requested it. At the end of the meeting, the organizer also asked me if she could pass on my email to those who were asking for more information. I agreed.

I was well aware of how so many people had assisted me

in my own battle with cancer. I had managed to put myself in the position where I had direct access to some of the leading scientists in cancer research. I knew that not everyone could be so fortunate. I saw it as my duty to help anyone I could.

Over the next few months, I received a phone call from a new cancer patient nearly every day — sometimes several in a single day. Many started to follow my suggestions to the letter. Some proved to be very good "students" indeed. A few months later, Bernard told me that my name had popped up time and again during his consultations. He said that many of his patients were doing better as a result of following my advice, naturally under strict medical supervision at all times. I was amazed and delighted to hear this.

I also began to get something of a reputation as an expert among my airline colleagues. It appeared that everybody had a cancer story to tell or knew somebody who had recently been diagnosed. It seemed that on every flight, at least one member of the crew would ask if they could speak to me in private about my approach to health, either for themselves or for someone close to them.

I started to give mini talks during our stopovers. Attendance was noncompulsory, but it surprised me to no end when, despite jet lag, so many of my colleagues turned up to listen to what I had to say. I handed out my personal phone number to these people as well, happy to pass on my experience and insights.

However, once at home, when I was supposed to be resting ahead of my next flight, I was becoming increasingly exhausted. The hours spent talking to other cancer sufferers, advising them on how to fast and what to eat, were wearing me out. At times, I felt as if I were standing alone on the beach facing a tsunami. There were so many patients and, I was surprised to find, doctors from other countries asking for my help. I feared I would drown in messages before I could respond to them all.

The hardest part for me was that so many people were calling me when they were in advanced stages of cancer, and at their most desperate. In many cases, their doctors had told them that nothing more could be done. In an ideal world, I would like people to adopt my protocol before they get sick.

Among the many messages I received, one will remain imprinted upon my mind forever. I had been contacted by the husband of a woman who had multi-metastatic cancer. She had undergone surgery, which involved her being opened up and then quickly closed again, once the surgeon realized that nothing could be done for her. Her husband said that she had been given forty-eight hours to live.

Unfortunately, I hadn't come across the message until several days after it was sent, since it had been buried beneath so many others. However, upon reading this devastating news, I contacted the husband with a degree of trepidation, fearful that I was too late. Nevertheless, he was happy to hear from me. He told me that his wife had been following my guidelines to the letter and was currently on her twenty-first day of fasting. She so far had exceeded her life expectancy by nearly three weeks.

I was so touched by the woman's story. She was only in her forties and had two young children, and I wanted to help in any way that I could. I had a brief conversation with her.

"I'm still here," she said, adding, "and I feel better than ever."

Her voice was weak, but determined, so I put a plan in place for her. It comprised a "gentle" ketogenic diet, allowing a few more carbs than usual. She slowly began to reintroduce food. We kept in contact via WhatsApp whenever she needed more advice or encouragement. After about two weeks, the messages became less frequent until a few days passed when I heard nothing. It was probably around three weeks after the initial contact that I received a heartbreaking message from the lady's husband.

He told me that his wife had passed away, but he ended by thanking me for what I'd done. He said that I'd enabled his family to have closure. I was shattered to hear that she hadn't made it, but her husband reassured me that those additional six weeks had given his wife the most precious gift that she could have wished for: the gift of time. Time spent with her loved ones, giving her children a memory of their mother and an opportunity to prepare for her passing that they otherwise would not have had.

Even though I had helped this woman and several other individuals, it became apparent to me that I needed to find a way to share my protocol with a larger audience—doctors and patients alike. It seemed crazy to me that so many researchers, brilliant in their own fields, had little knowledge of what their colleagues were doing. I recalled an early conversation

I'd had with Dr. William Li, when I'd told him about the keto-genic work being carried out by Professor Thomas Seyfried, who also happens to live in Boston. I'd then spoken about Professor Valter Longo and fasting. I recalled the surprise in Dr. Li's voice.

"JJ, you're a pioneer," he'd exclaimed. "We're all focused on our own thing."

This comment planted the seed of an idea in my mind which finally began to germinate in October 2016, when I started to think about how I could arrange a way to put all of these experts in one room, so they could share their experience and learn from one another. I wanted to create a super team that could build on one another's knowledge and research and come up with ways to fight cancer and other illnesses with greater efficacy. I figured that perhaps by bringing them together, so that they could share information, we could eventually find the best complementary approaches that could work in tandem with traditional medicine. But to make this dream a reality, I needed a platform.

One of my favorite sayings is by Japanese poet Ryunosuke Satoro: *Individually, we are one drop. Together, we are an ocean.*

This resonated with me more than ever before. It was while having these thoughts that I also came across another saying, this time by one of my all-time heroes, former South African President and Nobel Peace Prize winner Nelson Mandela.

He said, *"Even if you have a terminal disease, you don't have to sit down and mope. Enjoy life and challenge the illness that you have."*

Spurred on by these motivational words, I decided to take up the challenge.

I approached each of the doctors with whom I had built up a rapport in recent years. Doctors such as William Li, MD, president of the Angiogenesis Foundation; Valter Longo, who was gaining international renown as an expert on fasting; Thomas Seyfried, the leading figure on ketogenesis and metabolism; and several others. To my delight, each of them expressed their enthusiasm and said that they would happily attend a conference, provided I could cover the costs of them coming to France.

My next phone call was to Bernard Escudier. I repeated my plan to him and told him that I'd already lined up my dream team, as I now referred to them. There was silence on the end of the line, so I repeated my idea, thinking he might not have understood.

"I have a team in place," I said.

Still, silence.

I couldn't understand why he said nothing. Bernard had known Dr. William Li for many years, since they worked on the first angiogenic treatments together. He was surprised to hear that I had called these busy doctors and researchers and had gotten them to agree to come to France to support my cause.

Finally, he spoke. "Okay," he replied with characteristic pragmatism. "How are we going to do it?"

We brainstormed for the next few minutes and, by the end of the conversation, Bernard had agreed to approach

Professor Alexander Eggermont, general director of Institut Gustave Roussy (IGR) and renowned Dutch oncologist. If Eggermont agreed, we would hold the conference at IGR. Bernard also proposed to get in touch with the Accor Hotel Group, with whom he had a direct contact. All being well, the hotel accommodation and venue would then be taken care of. For my part, I said that I would approach the president of Air France to ask if he would agree to sponsor the flights.

My next step was to arrange an appointment with the new president of Air France, Jean-Marc Janaillac. I figured it would be difficult to get in touch with him, since he had only been in his position for a couple of weeks. Nevertheless, I wrote him a lengthy email, outlining everything that had happened to me and how I now wanted to share my experience for the good of many. I told him how I had the backing of leading doctors and scientists who were keen to come to France for a conference. I nervously read the email through several times, wanting each word to make the right impact, before finally clicking on "send."

Monsieur Janaillac got back to me just three days later. He said that he was no biologist and would therefore like me to contact his assistant to set up a meeting so that I could explain things in person.

Bursting with excitement, I immediately called Bernard and told him that he needed to free up his calendar. I felt that it was essential for him to come with me to meet the president of Air France, since this would decide whether or not the conference could take place. If we were unable to get Air

France to sponsor the flights, I couldn't imagine how else we would be able to cover the cost.

A couple of weeks later, Bernard and I sat in Mr. Janaillac's office. Impressed by my efforts to date, Mr. Janaillac agreed to look into having Air France fly the doctors to France. As I left the president's office, I felt dizzy at the momentum of events unfolding. From my initial idea just a few weeks earlier, it appeared all systems were a go for the conference to take place — one I hoped would lead to new breakthroughs in cancer treatment. I was excited, but I tried to keep my emotions in check. I had much work to do!

Some three weeks later, Mr. Janaillac's assistant got back to me with the green light. Bernard and I then conferred with the key speakers and set a date. It would be held in about six months, on September 21 at Institut Gustave Roussy in Paris, which barely gave us time to organize everything. With the main costs, such as the flights, hotels and venue, covered, we still had to find funds to cover additional expenses, such as meals, official media recordings, and transportation to and from the hotels. Somehow, I would have to get further funding. But how?

On a wet Sunday afternoon, while sitting together on the sofa and watching The X Factor, a talent show, on TV, Heather and I started brainstorming with the idea of how to raise money.

"Imagine if all those people out there were to donate to my conference, rather than voting for their favorite acts!" I exclaimed.

"Well ... what about crowdfunding?" Heather asked.

I had no idea what she was talking about until she proceeded to enlighten me. I'll be the first to admit that I'm not exactly computer savvy. Put me in the cockpit of an airplane surrounded by panels of complicated-looking dials, and I feel totally at home. Put me in front of an unfamiliar program on my Apple Mac ... well that's another story! Fortunately, Heather is great at this side of things. She helped me to set up a GoFundMe page. Together we wrote about my project and then, when everything was in place, I clicked the button to make it go live. I went to bed that evening with a sense of satisfaction tinged with apprehension. I was glad we'd gotten it done, but I did not anticipate donations arriving any time soon.

The next morning, I awoke to a flurry of activity on my iPhone. Friends from around the world had sent me messages of congratulations on my campaign. Many had donated generous sums of money. Barely awake, I quickly logged onto GoFundMe. Donations had been flooding in all night, amounting to several hundreds of dollars by mid-morning.

"Great initiative. Best of luck with the event," wrote one donor.

"My very best wishes for a successful conference. This may help so many people," wrote another.

"This is one amazing story that needs to be told. Keep up the good fight," wrote yet another.

I excitedly spent the next few hours watching the site as the amount collected continued to rise. Donations ranged from 10 dollars to 300 dollars or more, and they came from friends and strangers all over the world. Before long, the campaign was becoming so popular that I received a call from GoFundMe France. A member of their marketing department contacted me to say that mine was one of the fastest growing and most impressive campaigns on their platform. As a result, they offered to provide additional publicity for me. I couldn't believe what was happening, but I took it as an indication of how important this conference would be. I felt that a revolution was about to take place.

CHAPTER 19

Rethinking Cancer 2017

ON THE MORNING OF the Rethinking Cancer 2017 conference, I sat at the side of the stage listening to the opening address by Bernard Escudier, my doctor and friend and the chairman of renal cancer at Institut Gustave Roussy, which also was our venue for the day. Bernard and I had come a long way since 2012, when my initial kidney cancer became metastatic and sent malignant tumors on a rampant invasion of my lungs. Back then, he hadn't expected me to survive more than a few months. We had spoken of possibly putting me on a course of immunotherapy, which would have ended my flying career. Instead I'd opted for surgery, an antiangiogenic eating plan combined with a ketogenic diet, a daily intake of spirulina, and fasting.

I remembered Bernard's reaction when I'd first told him about the fasting, how he had smiled and said that it was, *"bon pour la ligne"* (good for the silhouette). And yet, to his great credit, Bernard had always been open-minded about my approaches and, when he saw the positive results, he acknowledged my success and further opened his mind. I know how lucky I have been to have such an oncologist at my side, since doctors like Bernard tend to be the exception rather than the rule.

As I listened to Bernard's words at the start of the conference, I glanced along the first row of the audience, reserved for invited speakers. It looked like a Who's Who of medicine. In scientific circles, medical researchers are revered as some kind of demigods, rock stars in lab coats. These brilliant people are so intent on finding a cure for disease that they immerse themselves deeply in their work and rarely converse with "regular people." Yet they all had carved out time in their hectic schedules for a conference made possible by a crowd-funding campaign organized by my wife and me, as well as the generous sponsorship of Air France, flying all the presenters in for free, and the Pullman Hotel Bercy, which had provided the accommodations for our speakers.

Never before had a leading cancer institute publicly embraced alternative approaches to cancer treatment. The medical professionals who came had put aside their own egos to listen to one another and to share ideas, because I was living proof that different approaches can be more effective when used in synergy.

Just six months prior, Rethinking Cancer 2017 had been

a mere seed of an idea, but on September 21, 2017, at Institut Gustave Roussy, in an auditorium filled with three hundred people, including doctors, medical students and patients, it had become an exciting reality. Word of the conference had been spread via the cancer institute, as well as my GoFundMe page and a dedicated Facebook page that Heather had set up for me. Now the time was ripe to share and collaborate.

The date had been heavily circled on my calendar for months and, when it finally arrived, it's hard to describe how I felt. In the months leading up to the conference, life had been busy. In addition to helping to put the event together, I had qualified as a captain on the Airbus A380, the world's largest commercial passenger plane. It had been a huge personal achievement, particularly in light of my medical history, but it nevertheless felt miniscule compared to what was about to unfold. Now I just wanted to get on with it!

As I again looked out across the front row and mentally noted some of the world's leading scientists, I realized many were now at the top of my WhatsApp contact list. Conversations which had started out as a quest to find answers for my own health had evolved into friendships where I was made privy to their latest findings before they were published. Among the familiar faces of that front row was Dr. William Li, president of the Angiogenesis Foundation. His passion had captivated me when I stumbled upon his 2010 TED Talk, *Can We Eat to Starve Cancer?* Hearing him describe how we can "eat to beat" changed the way I think about food and what I put on my plate.

Then there was Professor Valter Longo, the leading expert on fasting in relation to cancer. I remembered the first time I saw him give an interview in the fascinating French documentary entitled *Le jêune, une nouvelle therapie* (English title: "Science of Fasting"), where he presented the idea that you could reboot your immune system by starving yourself. I'd tried out his theory and was able to kill off tumors in my lungs that otherwise could have killed me.

Next my eyes fell upon Professor Laurence Zitvogel, a pioneer in the field of tumor immunology and cancer immunotherapy.

Shortly before the conference was due to start, Professor Zitvogel had taken me aside and asked for a couple of minutes in private. She'd been unable to conceal the excitement in her voice, so of course, I'd agreed.

"I've got your results," she stated, showing me pages of a document detailing the bacteria found in my microbiome. "You have a good number of bacteria that are known anti-inflammatory agents, but there are two that we were unable to identify."

I let the information sink in. Three months previously I had given a stool sample so that my gut bacteria could be analyzed in the lab. The results now seemed to be an indication that my protocol may have created a new type of bacteria. *But which part of it could have effected the change?* I wondered.

As if reading my thoughts, she continued, "It's a shame we didn't test your bacteria before you started taking phycocyanin." She went on to explain that she was considering the fact that the light-harvesting protein, extracted from spirulina, might have played an important role in the transformation, adding that she would be prepared to start lab tests once funding became available. Now, she had my rapt attention.

"My team has proposed that we name one of the bacteria *Zitvogelus*," she said with a parting laugh.

Seated next to Professor Zitvogel was her husband and fellow researcher, Professor Guido Kroemer, a cell biologist of international renown.

Also present, among many others, were highly respected French oncologist Dr. Laurent Schwarz, whose work on the metabolic treatment of cancer has generated a great deal of interest; Ulrike Kammerer, German doctor and expert on the ketogenic diet; Rainer Stange, representing Professor Andreas Michalsen, chief physician at the department of naturopathy at Berlin's Immanuel Hospital; and pioneering American researcher Professor Adrienne Scheck, who is recognized for her work using the ketogenic approach in the treatment of malignant brain tumors.

I then saw the towering figure of Dr. David Quinn, medical director at Norris Cancer hospital, who had played the crucial role of authorizing Professor Longo's findings on fasting to be tested in the first clinical trials worldwide.

Looking at Dr. Quinn, I recalled the previous night and how he had entertained me with humorous stories, told in his distinctive Australian accent, at our group dinner at the famous *Cafe de l'Homme*. The restaurant, often referred to as the most beautiful terrace in Paris, is located on the iconic *Place du Trocadéro* and opposite the Eiffel Tower.

We'd continued to converse as the sun went down and dusk set in. The Eiffel Tower put on its hourly breathtaking display, puncturing the darkness with a multitude of lights flickering like diamonds. Our group let out a collective gasp followed by the sound of scraping chairs as many of these brilliant medical minds grabbed hold of their mobile phones and stood to position themselves, so that they could record the beauty of the spectacle unfolding before their eyes. This very human moment had made me realize that, irrespective of their countless distinctions and awards, I was surrounded by people with good hearts and honest intentions, people who were excited by life and its endless possibilities.

Sitting in the auditorium listening to Bernard give his welcome speech, I sensed that same feeling of excitement and wonder I'd witnessed in the scientists the night before. But now each had come to share and to hear about one another's pioneering approaches to cancer treatment.

Bernard finished his opening address and handed the platform over to the general director of IGR, Alexander Eggermont, or "Lex" as he is known to his friends. An easy-going Dutchman, Lex began by saying kind words about me, which caught me somewhat off guard.

"It shows what a person can do, in supporting a cause and thinking in an innovative way, to get people together at a site which is dedicated to innovation and the access to innovation," he said.

He elaborated by stating that Institut Gustave Roussy is the largest comprehensive cancer center in Europe, with the largest program for bringing new treatments—and access to treatments—to patients. His words underlined the significance of the venue that we'd chosen for the conference. I felt humbled and a little embarrassed. I never wanted any of this to be about me. After seeing results for my own health, I had become passionate about empowering my fellow patients in their fight against cancer and other illnesses. That is all. My mission was—and still is—to help educate physicians and patients alike, so they can share new approaches in treatment to complement traditional medicine for the benefit of everyone.

Lex then went on to give an engaging introduction, talking about the tiny village of Acciaroli in southern Italy, in which an unusually high proportion of the inhabitants live to be one hundred years old or more. This aged population eats locally grown, pesticide-free produce and consumes plenty of olive oil and herbs. Lex added that there is much truth to the words, "You are what you eat." I was struck by how refreshing it was for the director of Europe's top cancer center to focus so much of his talk around food, rather than obsess over the latest developments in expensive drugs and chemotherapy.

When it was my turn to step out onto the stage, I felt calm and focused. I guess you could say I switched into pilot mode. I knew that my job at that moment was to get this "plane" off the runway, to get the conference started and to enable the dream team to take to the skies.

As I prepared to stand up to the microphone, I felt my father's gold ring, heavy on the second finger of my right hand. As always, its presence gave great comfort to me. As I remembered my father and how he had guided me through life, I again felt his spirit with me. I briefly touched the ring, took a deep breath and stepped forward. Taking to the stage, I once more searched the sea of faces in front of me. I was greeted by reassuring smiles, and I knew that I was in the company of friends.

Looking from face to face, I again recalled how each of our shared journeys began. And why we all were there. For so long, everyone had been working away in their individual silos, blinded to what else was out there. All I had done was take what I considered to be the best parts of each approach and combine them for use in my own battle against cancer. And, as I write this, it seems to be working still.

After saying a few words, I returned to my seat and was overwhelmed by the applause from everyone present. It reminded me of the first time I'd spoken publicly of my protocol, at the previous year's A.R.Tu.R. conference in Paris. Once again, alongside the medical professionals, a large number of patients were present and looking to me for some kind of guidance. I still hadn't become accustomed to being the focus of so much attention.

I am a pilot and, as such, my job is to find solutions to problems. In my line of work, if something isn't working, then I have to fix it, and fast. Upon facing a problem with my health, I simply applied the same approach and did what I am naturally wired to do. To keep pushing further, to think above and beyond. Clearly modern cancer treatments are falling short, and yet here I am, more than fifteen years after my initial kidney cancer diagnosis, and still in good health. I am a stage four cancer survivor who seems to have found a better flight path than the one routinely chosen.

Rethinking Cancer 2017 enabled my dream team of specialists to board this flight with me, and I believe with all my heart and conviction that they are looking after everyone's best interests during this journey together.

The plane is still aloft. We have yet to arrive in the land of freedom from cancer, but if, at some time in the near future, we meet again to share results of new clinical trials for better and less invasive treatments, then I'll know we are flying in the right direction. And perhaps we will land a little farther afield next time.

ENDNOTES

1   Asperger's syndrome is named after Austrian
    pediatrician Hans Asperger (1906–1980), who, in
    1944, described four children in his practice who had
    difficulty with social interaction. It wasn't until almost
    fifty years later, in 1992, that AS became a standard
    diagnosis when it was included in the tenth edition of
    the World Health Organization's diagnostic manual,
    International Classification of Disease.

2   Wilhelmi de Toledo, F.; Grundler, F.; Bergouignan, A.;
    Drinda, S.; Michalsen, A. Safety, health improvement
    and well-being during a 4 to 21-day fasting period in
    an observational study including 1422 subjects. PLoS
    One, 2019, 14(01).

    Wilhelmi de Toledo, F.; Grundler, F.; Sirtori, C.R.;
    Ruscica, M. Unravelling the health effects of fasting:
    a long road from obesity treatment to healthy life span
    increase and improved cognition. Annals of
    Medicine, 2020.

Therapeutic Fasting: The Buchinger Amplius Method,
Thieme. ISBN: 9783131603616

3   Full disclosure: At the time of this writing, I am
    working with Xelliss, formerly Natura4Ever, as
    Brand Ambassador. I have chosen to do so because
    I am convinced of the benefits of spirulina and also
    phycocyanin in the maintenance of good health.
    Xelliss uses state-of-the-art technology, growing its
    spirulina in photobioreactors to ensure a product that
    is free from pathogens and toxins. The company uses
    its own exclusive strain of spirulina for cultivation to
    ensure premium quality at all times. I am aware that
    there are many different spirulina brands available
    and would suggest that the reader choose the brand
    with which they feel most comfortable. As with any
    food supplement, I would like to stress the importance
    of looking at where and how the product has been
    manufactured in order to make an informed choice.

ACKNOWLEDGMENTS

THIS BOOK WOULD NOT HAVE BEEN possible without the support of a great many special people. My apologies to any whom I have failed to mention, but I do appreciate each and every individual who has been involved in my personal cancer journey.

First and foremost, I would like to thank my wife, Heather, for always being at my side and riding out the highs and lows with me. Likewise, I wish to show my gratitude to my children, Kelly and Jeff, whose unconditional love kept me going even when I was in a very dark place. And, of course, I wish to acknowledge the love of my entire family, my siblings, Jean-Yves and Taina, but especially my parents, Jacques and Michèle.

I have dedicated this book to the memory of my father because I made promises to him, on his deathbed, that I would return to the cockpit and also continue to help anyone in need. I like to think he would be proud of what I have achieved in fulfilling those promises.

I would also like to use this opportunity to thank Robin Colucci, Polly Letofsky and Donna Mazzitelli, whose combined knowledge and expertise has been invaluable in the realization of this project.

Obviously, I owe my heartfelt appreciation to a whole host of doctors and researchers. The top of this list has to be my oncologist, Dr. Bernard Escudier, who has played a key role in my story since the emergence of metastatic tumors in my lungs in 2012. I am so grateful that I had the fortune to be under his medical care, and for his willingness to open his mind to things with which he was previously unfamiliar. Rethinking Cancer 2017 would not have been possible without his vision and immense generosity of spirit.

My endless gratitude should also be extended to the following brilliant minds, equally without whom the conference would not have taken place: Dr. William Li, Professor Valter Longo, Dr. David Quinn, Professor Laurence Zitvogel, Professor Guido Kroemer, Professor Thomas Seyfried, Dr. Adrienne Scheck, Dr. Rainer Stange, Professor Ulrike Kämmerer, Ulrike Gonder, Professor Monika Reuss-Borst and Dr. Matthew Williams.

Rethinking Cancer 2017 is available to watch on YouTube thanks to the talented husband and wife team, Thierry de Lestrade and Sylvie Gilman. Their fascinating film *Le Jêune, une nouvelle Thérapie ?* (English: The Science of Fasting) was instrumental in my discovery of key knowledge that has become an essential part of my personal protocol.

It is impossible to mention fasting without paying tribute to Dr. Francoise Wilhelmi de Toledo, director of Europe's leading therapeutic fasting clinic, The Buchinger Wilhelmi Clinic, and someone for whom I have immense admiration. Her groundbreaking work with Professor Andreas Michalsen of Charité Berlin, one of Europe's largest university hospitals, is paving the way for exciting new perspectives in the use of fasting for patients with specific pathologies.

I would additionally like to acknowledge Dr. Lawrence Schwartz and dietitian-nutritionist Magali Walkowicz for their relentless work on metabolism with an ever-increasing number of patients. Special thanks also goes to radiologist Dr. Francois Paziot, whose sharp eyes scrutinized my early scans and detected my initial kidney cancer. It was again Francois to whom I turned in 2012. His meticulous attention to detail no doubt contributed to saving my life and those of countless others.

Finally, I wish to extend my appreciation to Jean-Marc Janaillac, former president of Air France, and his successor, Benjamin Smith, both of whom embraced my campaign with their full and unwavering support. Indeed, I will finish by thanking Air France, the airline, for enabling me to pursue an amazing career, flying my fellow human beings to incredible destinations throughout the world. Never in my wildest dreams, as a young boy sitting behind my father in the cockpit of a DC-8, did I imagine I would one day have the chance to captain the world's largest passenger aircraft, the legendary A380. Thank you, Air France, for always believing in me.

Jean-Jacques Trochon
Biarritz, August 2020

ABOUT THE AUTHORS

JEAN-JACQUES TROCHON (or JJ as he is more commonly known) spent thirty-two years as a commercial airline pilot for Air France. A French national, he enjoyed an early childhood in Tahiti before finishing his schooling in France and the USA.

In 2003, JJ was diagnosed with aggressive kidney cancer and subsequently underwent the removal of his left kidney. In 2012 and 2014, he underwent further surgeries following the discovery of multiple metastases in both lungs. Despite being given a slim chance of survival, JJ again returned to work in 2016. He captained the world's largest commercial aircraft, the Airbus A380, until his retirement in spring 2020.

Today, JJ devotes his spare time to helping other cancer sufferers and spreading the word about his revolutionary approach to the disease. He was the initiator of Rethinking Cancer 2017, a groundbreaking conference held in Paris on September 21, 2017, at Institut Gustave Roussy, the leading cancer center in Europe.

When not researching the latest cancer treatments, JJ can be found cheering on the Springboks, his favorite rugby team, or surfing the waves near his home in the French Basque Country. For more information on his approach, or to book JJ as a motivational speaker, please check out his website, www.jeanjacquestrochon.com, or his Facebook page, rethinkingcancer2017.

HEATHER WHITEHALL-TROCHON is a lover of languages and translator of French and German into English. A British national, she completed studies in fashion journalism at the London College of Fashion before moving to Munich, Germany, where she worked in public relations for fashion and film. After relocating to Vienna, Austria, she had a brief stint as an editor at the Associated Press, prior to becoming a freelance translator and seasoned backpacker. Heather met JJ in Paris in 2007, marrying him the following year. The couple, together with their cat, Zulu, have now settled in Biarritz, France.

JJ's memoir is Heather's first book, but she plans to dedicate more time to writing in the future. When not sitting behind her computer screen, Heather loves nothing more than morning swims in the Atlantic Ocean. She is also a passionate collector of vintage clothing, most notably from the 1970s, and has been known to spontaneously break into a dance move whenever she hears an ABBA song on the radio.

Printed by Amazon Italia Logistica S.r.l.
Torrazza Piemonte (TO), Italy

16673533R00148